Lost for 72,000 Miles

Parallel Journey

by

P. G. Wood

Dad, you live in me, and in my book.

Mum, no one else understood my humour the way you did.

Aims

I hope to communicate my thoughts, emotions, experiences and needs. I aim to give life to the people I describe and the places I have visited.

This is not a book to provide any form of self-help and I am certainly not looking to earn any type of prestige, approval or appreciation. I am not here to impress or leave any kind of mark on the world. I only hope to offer something meaningful and I have written with sincerity.

Importantly, I am not intending to hurt anyone, seek revenge, to libel or defame any person. Hence, all the characters described have fictitious names.

This is a story based on real-life events.

I have indicated the southern linguistic features (drawl) in the dialogue passages only where I felt it was necessary to give the reader examples of the challenges that I faced understanding the stronger local dialect and differences in language, and for the North Carolinians to understand my accent and language. Where the dialogue has not been inflicted with the accent, this is partly for ease of reading and also indicates the accent was not that strong and was easier to understand due to the passage of time or that I did not have problems making myself understood.

I am treading water in a cold and deep ocean.

I am growing tired.

There are no ripples on the surface; and I do not panic.

Looking around, I can see land in the far distance.

I do not have the strength to swim back to the shore.

P.G. Wood 2015

In memory of Sylvia

Prologue

It was my last present to open and I wanted to save the biggest until last, even though I had no idea what was inside. I excitedly tore off the wrapping paper revealing a box containing a board game called The Game of Life and as I opened the lid, I was overpowered by the fresh smells. American-styled, white, plastic, matchbox-sized universities, chapels, bridges and monuments slotted into place as I eagerly set up the board game for the whole family to play, as Nana started falling asleep.

Each person in my family chose a small different coloured plastic car, and I was left with the green one. The small blue peg fitted into a hole on the right side of the car – the driving seat – and I spun the wheel of fortune, which made a strange clicking noise and stopped on a random number, and my journey along a road divided into squares, through a temporary life began. When I landed on my first square, it produced laughter and the odd grumble depending whether it was a good or a bad square.

The game simulated a person's journey through life, from college to retirement, with jobs, marriage, possible children and various challenges along the way; and the aim was to reach that happy old age, achieving nice things along the travels in his or her life – a big deal, in a child's mind.

If only each journey in life could start with a 'warm up', the playing of some kind of board game – and then real life and its challenges could return to the box!

Journeys through real life have 'bad squares', and we might have the talents to jump over life's hurdles, sometimes with the greatest of ease. We can run without looking back, or forget that these challenges ever existed. Some of us struggle over them, get tangled or stumble, doing our best to pick ourselves up, dust ourselves down and continue

1

in the direction that life takes us. We may have the life-skills to provide us with the determination to carry on – preparing us for future challenges that life throws at us.

It does not matter what position in society we have, we all experience challenge.

1

June 1993

Reflections of red-brick buildings, surrounded by the barren, wind-swept Pennines and blanketed under grey skies: an all too familiar image disappearing in the shuddering rear-view mirror, as I drove away from my hometown – away from my past!

As I sped up, happy childhood memories flooded my mind, of my younger brother and I, huddled around a blazing coal fire, wearing pyjamas, as we watched TV and played with our toys, whilst our dad cooked Christmas dinner.

As my journey on the motorway progressed, I thought more about my dad: a divorced man bringing up two children on his own, yet working full time. I never appreciated how difficult this must have been and how dedicated he was: bringing up children is demanding for any one person, but for a man, in the 1970s, it was unheard of. Few of my friends had divorced parents and my family situation often made me feel embarrassed, yet I feel more ashamed now, for thinking like that then. I always tried to keep it a secret from everyone and it was difficult pretending as I grew older.

I thought about my dad for most of the journey to London – I was, in fact, leaving home.

He was a 'gentleman' and a gentle man, always putting my brother and me first, and he worked tirelessly all of his life. He was generous, humble, and had seen little of life outside of Rochdale. For a man of small stature, he had a big heart.

Money was always tight and opportunities difficult to attain, yet having a humble background only fuelled my determination to make something of myself. I had an ambitious outlook on life and as I grew older, I persevered with this inner drive, achieving what I wanted, through education – my passport.

After hours of driving my old Ford Capri and reflecting upon my childhood, I arrived in a busy London – my destination. They call the Ford Capri, the 'poor man's sports car' – I had just fifty pounds in my back pocket.

As I stopped in traffic on Regent Street, I admired the grandiose buildings and noticed people standing around taking photographs, the neon signs, the Shaftesbury memorial and statues of two majestic horses to my right – a main central tourist attraction – and thought, this was worlds apart from Rochdale!

Piccadilly Circus is famous for notable buildings, including the London Pavilion and Criterion Theatre, where people meet from 'four corners of the world': a change from the much slower pace of life in my northern hometown.

I noticed a sea of people in Trafalgar Square, huge decorative fountains and The National Gallery in the background with its plinths and pillars – small details emphasised by the shadows in the late afternoon sunshine.

I strained and squinted as looked up at Nelson's Column which towered over me against a bright blue sky and white fluffy clouds, but I was unable to see Nelson at the top from my low position.

The traffic moved, but I was in awe of everything around me, displayed in bright daylight. A man in a car behind beeped his horn several times in frustration, reminding me to drive on, as I remained transfixed. Maybe this was his hometown, and he was taking everything for granted or in a hurry. In comparison, a feeling of euphoria flowed through my veins.

I could not wait to visit the endless choice of museums and art galleries, explore the streets full of shops, sit in the countless cafes and read books, meet new people and start a new chapter of my life.

I drove down Whitehall, noticing the entrance of 10 Downing Street, partly obscured by a crowd of people in front of its protective tall black painted gates (waiting for a peek of John Major). Each building I drove past had its unique place in British history and position in this part of London – so different to the centre of Rochdale. The only building I admired was Rochdale Town Hall – a striking example of gothic architecture that Adolf Hitler wanted to pull down, transport to Germany and rebuild.

The car had failed its MOT days earlier and was beyond repair. It made painful whining sounds on its last journey. Within days of arriving in London, I called a mechanic who took it to a scrapyard – its final destination. The car was worthless, but I had arrived, taking a chance in life and a boot loaded with belongings.

Julia (who I once shared a house with at polytechnic) now lived in a compact bedsit and worked for a small advertising company. A bubbly and rather eccentric character, she was newly married, although not living with her husband (which was 'different').

Julia had told me about this smaller empty furnished room next to hers, several weeks ago. She said on the phone, 'What have you got to lose?', which had inspired me to take the opportunity to live in London. She spoke to the landlord on my behalf, who agreed that I could stay in the bedsit and claim housing benefit, whilst seeking employment. I never did meet him.

The bright city lights of London had a pull on me ever since I visited the capital on a sixth-form trip ten years earlier. I remembered walking around large buildings and looking down, thinking aloud: 'I am walking on the ground in London' – an absurd remark yet a surreal sensation. Here I was again, a decade later: living off benefits, eating toast and drinking tea, being alone all day in my tiny top-floor bedsit, in a pebble-dashed building within walking distance of Clapham South tube station and a short journey into a hectic Charing Cross.

To pass time during the day and to avoid spending what little money I had, I walked around the local areas of Clapham and Balham or sat in parks to read library books. The London parks and commons were brimming with people, especially at the weekends or on warm evenings – spending time in a park was a very different pastime to my northern upbringing. I noticed solitary people sat on opposite ends of park benches, engrossed in their books or just watching the world go by. In London, it did not seem 'odd' to be on your own.

On a warm Saturday afternoon, I took yet another solitary walk onto a busy Clapham Common. Julia had gone away for the weekend to see her husband (as she always did). I carried a book and sat down on a park bench on the south side of the Common but ended up spending most of my time wondering if I would 'survive' this summer in London.

I still had no money or job and I knew nobody. Most days, I would spend time at the local job centre in Balham, and afterwards I always looked forward to Julia coming home from work. I had the weekends to myself but today, I was feeling lonely. I missed my family, friends and the familiarity of my hometown. Maybe, there were other people sitting in this park who felt the same way I did.

After some time thinking about my new circumstances, I decided I would just see out this summer of 1993, and if my situation had not improved, then I would return home to Rochdale. I still had no plans of a career, despite having a BSc in Environmental Science under my belt, which would have been impossible to achieve without receiving a maintenance grant.

I looked around at the trees in full leaf. It was pleasant as I sat in the warm weather to read my library book (*The Wasp Factory* by Iain Banks). I stared at the first page, unable to focus on any of the text. I tried to read the first paragraph but closed the book in frustration, putting it down next to me as I looked around again, at the massive open space. There was nothing particularly distracting me, but I still felt an element of excitement, thinking there was a vast city out there, full of opportunities.

A tall, slim man in his mid-twenties sauntered past me and I looked up at him. He looked back down at me as I remained seated on the park bench. Dressed in a plain white T-shirt and jeans, he carried on walking. I looked down at my book, opening it again to the first page.

I continued to stare at the text, then looked to my left at the tall man who was now sitting on the next park bench. He looked over, and saw me looking at him and smiled. I felt strange inside and looked down at my book, pretending not to notice.

I reacted strangely by standing up and walking away in the opposite direction, and then, I sat down again, on the next empty park bench. Despite the intrigue of this situation, I was nervous and the tall stranger remained seated with his long arms stretched out.

In my peripheral vision, someone walked past me and as I glanced upwards, I saw the tall man again, who appeared to be smirking as he walked, and as he looked back, I smiled in response. He turned the corner and disappeared from view.

My curiosity got the better of me and I closed my book, stood up and walked in the same direction. When I came to the intersection of the concrete path, I looked to my right and saw him standing under a massive oak tree. Despite his white T-shirt, it was hard to see him, as the tree's heavy branches hung low, blocking out the late afternoon sunlight.

Not knowing what to expect, as this situation did not feel real – a man flirting with me in broad daylight – I felt excited, as if I had been transported back in time, to middle school, having my first crush on a girl. I was fascinated and transfixed by her, despite not knowing her. I remembered her face: full lips, wide eyes, pale skin and red hair shining in the sunlight. Those distant feelings were just as intense as that encounter in the park, but it was not just some schoolchild crush. I was just as confused about my sexuality at school as I was at that moment.

My senses seemed 'sharpened' – maybe from the effects of adrenaline flowing through every single blood vessel and my heart felt heavy.

He walked further into the maze of the trees, and my instincts told me to follow him into the shadows and as the light dimmed, I stooped under the low-lying branch until I reached a small clearing under another large tree. The foliage was denser. Here I was, in the darkness and quietness of the trees, sheltered from the brightness and openness of Clapham Common teaming with families, children, pets, joggers, and lonely people, all surrounded by the busy streets of London.

My breathing shallowed and my skin tingled. I could hear and feel the surge of blood as my heart pounded, aware of everyone around me yet focused on one person.

I stooped underneath another low-lying branch and walked around the large tree in the dappled sunlight. I could sense him on the other side of the trunk. I stood silently and waited with eyes wide, not knowing what to expect. I could hear him breathing and felt electricity running through my body. With lips numb and mouth dry, I was confused; I wanted to run, I wanted to remain still. I wanted attention yet I wanted to hide.

I was scared, intrigued, confused and excited, and I had never experienced feelings like this. Feeling euphoric, I thought about the bullies back in my school days: hurling cruel abuse, laughing, making me feel ashamed of who and what I was. Now, I wanted to laugh back in their faces and in my mind, I towered over them and all the teachers, rising high above the school, into the sky, looking down feeling pity for every single person. I had become a monumental dragon, breathing hot flames, scorching the school field and all of the bullies who stood on it. This moment felt intense. I closed my eyes, and did not want to move – this was animalistic. Immobile as a statue, despite the chemistry inside me working overtime, my pounding heart distorted my whole chest.

He moved slowly and deliberately around the trunk of the tree, standing motionless, inches away from me. This had turned into some kind of predator–prey relationship, and I was not sure who was who. I felt transfixed and exhilarated yet trembled with anticipation. He edged towards me and I could feel the tree trunk's hard ridges pressing into my back. He slowly moved closer, staring, until I could feel his warm breath. I closed my eyes.

2

August 1993

Before we parted on that late Saturday afternoon on Clapham Common, he gave me his business card, and after several days of hesitation, I called him. Several weeks later, I had a full-time clerical job, and by the time late summer arrived, I had entered into a new relationship with the man who kissed me under the oak tree.

Philip Stevenson was six-foot four, unassumingly handsome and confident. He worked in the City, owned a small flat in Battersea and had a nice circle of friends. This was my first gay relationship, and even though it took time to adjust to this new lifestyle, I was quickly drawn into his way of life. That unassuming shy northern schoolboy, who nobody wanted to speak to, who kept his eyes down and mind to himself had transformed into an outgoing 27-year-old man with Mediterranean good looks, who was surprised at the attention he now received: the ugly duckling had transformed into a beautiful swan.

At school, I had felt ashamed of my olive skin and wavy brown hair and tried to blow-dry my hair straight, as well as using talcum powder on my face to make me look paler. I wanted to blend in with the majority at school and everyone on my council estate.

Growing up, I felt different and unpopular, experiencing prolonged and often painful bullying. The words 'puff' or 'queer' became everyday phrases hurled at me and often said with hatred – the bullies made their decisions quickly, labelling me from an early age, categorising who I was and what I was, even though I had not yet fully understood myself.

I desperately wanted to be 'normal', like other boys: I tried having girlfriends, they were a smoke screen. I yearned to play football but I didn't have the sporting skills, to partake in fights but despised violence, to smoke cigarettes with the in-crowd but that only made me cough. I wanted to be a sporting hero – accepting trophies given out in end-of-year school assemblies, that heterosexual, popular boys received from equally alpha-male PE teachers or a proud headmaster. I remember how confidently they walked across a creaking wooden stage in the school hall, receiving a masculine gratuitous handshake, a wink or a manly pat on the back, quickly followed by a rapturous applause and whistles from their adoring fans, announcing them as 'heroes' – they had status.

I wanted to block out the painful reminders of school, and, most importantly, feeling different to everyone else. I did not want attention and was conscious my voice sounded too effeminate. I purposely failed tests, in case the teacher would say 'Well done!' I just wanted to be a normal teenage boy. School is supposed to be the best time of your life.

Within weeks of arriving in London, Phil and I were practically living together. In retrospect, I probably moved in with him too quickly but he loved me and offered security. I felt protected and loved him and this new way of life: designer clothes, expensive gifts, holidays, private viewings in art galleries, socialite parties, all-night clubbing and smoking cigarettes, seducing me into a fantasy world.

This new life in London and all its trappings was, indeed, a complete transformation. I had never felt attractive and now I did – I had never been popular and now I turned heads, and it was hard to believe.

I hid this relationship from family and friends back in Rochdale did not know of my other life in London. I was not embarrassed about Phil, but ashamed of my personal life in the middle-class fast lane that turned out to be 'superficial' and polarising from my previous life in Rochdale.

Around April 2000, the relationship ran its course – the river ran dry – and although this was a shock, especially losing the security, I got over him. Eventually, after some difficulties, we became friends.

Phil kindly allowed me to live with him until I found my feet, which I appreciated, although, looking back, it must have been a complicated and awkward situation, especially for him. However, he had a positive influence on my life, although I was too stubborn to realise it then. He helped to shape me into the person I am today.

That past life felt like a 'fantasy' world.

3

October 2000

It was a year full of changes. After breaking up with Phil and still living with him (for some time), I decided to apply for a mortgage, and in October, I met someone new, which inadvertently blossomed into a relationship.

Nick Robinson was twelve years younger, and had dark hair and brown eyes positioned closely together, a square-jaw, full lips, a heavy brow, was six-foot two, slim, handsome yet shy. He dressed in business suits at work, but at home he wore tracksuits. He was unfashionable and socially awkward but I gravitated towards him quickly, literally turning my world upside down.

At first, I felt insecure about the age difference but assumed these doubts were natural feelings, as being with someone considerably younger encompassed a range of insecurities and more awareness of our differences; however, he made me feel uplifted and energised. I stopped wearing designer clothes and being the 'trophy' boyfriend. I wanted to be more like him - quiet and unassuming. This relationship made me feel at ease with others around me, including close family.

Generally, I was happier and this new relationship with Nick eventually gave me the confidence to 'come out' to family and close friends; I was proud to be with him.

My dad met him several times and treated him as a family member and was always asking about him. I had reached the pinnacle of my own contentment: my love for Nick overcoming the differences between us. From my perspective this was pure love, feeling fulfilled, feeling perfect.

Nick had flaws (just like everybody) but I respected him. He was not outwardly gay, which was refreshing. My sexual orientation no longer seemed defined, ending feelings of vulnerability. Dating Nick brought out my masculinity and femininity, sometimes filling a more 'feminine' role within the dynamics of our gay relationship, alternating the spectrum of my sexuality, yet I enjoyed my niche – a new identity.

Nick had lost his mother at an early age, which fitted with my natural tendency to 'mother' him. This developed into caring for him, cooking for him, being there for him, and in a bizarre way, I was happy to do these things. He was the technophile, I was the technophobe; he dressed down, and I dressed up; yet, despite these differences and numerous others, he brought out the best in me. Simply, life had become harmonious.

Phil had also met someone new and I was happy for him, although it felt strange after being with him for such a long time, and I eventually told him about my new relationship with Nick. It was now time to make a life of my own and after several months of saving and some delays, Phil kindly helped me finally move into a one-bedroom flat in south-west London in January 2001 and when I said goodbye to him, he gave me a bottle of champagne and two flutes – a meaningful and special gift. In addition, my teaching career was going well, and I had made a small circle of reliable gay and straight friends. Nick moved in several months later, following a whirlwind romance.

After several short trips away and 18 months later, Nick and I had planned a holiday to South Africa in April 2002. However, an unexplained strain developed between us and we seemed to argue over trivialities, so I nearly cancelled the holiday. On reflection, I was probably more at fault in my frustration, as at the time, I had no idea what was causing these problems. He seemed increasingly distant and sometimes arrived home late from work. Maybe our differences were finally taking their toll.

South Africa would either make us or break us.

4

April 2002

I stared into two large empty wine glasses, glistening in the late afternoon sunlight as I reflected on the last day of our holiday in South Africa.

A waiter promptly arrived. He was tall, in his early twenties and seemed shy. His fitted white shirt emphasised his lean body and he smiled graciously as he carried a bottle of red wine on a small silver tray and skilfully poured a small amount of the wine into my glass before tentatively placing it on the table.

'Thank you', I politely smiled, looking up at him after tasting the rich, full-bodied wine.

He then cautiously poured wine, half filling each glass, smiled and walked away.

Over the last two weeks, we had driven a hired car for hundreds of miles past breath-taking landscapes, staying overnight at different hotels on the long journey. The scenery had been truly magnificent: mountains, valleys, open plains, vineyards, coastlines, amazing viewpoints of the Cape of Good Hope and incredible vistas of the Atlantic Ocean – a country that seemed to offer everything you could possibly imagine.

We visited an elephant park and drove past never-ending forests. We sampled fine wines on the tour (a prerequisite of this trip), stopping off at recommended, and not so recommended, picturesque wineries along the route but I was still no closer to being a wine connoisseur.

Moreover, we seemed to enjoy our South African adventure. The wine tour had ended, and we finally relaxed in Cape Town, before we were due to fly back to London and our normal lives.

We felt exhausted as we sat at a table in a steak house on the waterfront; it had an excellent view of the harbour littered with boats and yachts of all shapes, sizes and value. The same waiter returned, this time balancing two large white plates. Presented in a contemporary style, the food tasted good. The atmosphere in the restaurant was pleasant, yet Nick was quiet.

Earlier, at the hotel, Nick said he had a 'bad stomach', which resulted in no physicality between us. On a couple of occasions, I had picked up strange feelings of hostility, especially when we just went straight to sleep at night, and on another occasion, when we had stopped in the car in front of a never-ending forest, on our journey across the plains of Stellenbosch.

I hoped we would go and look at a giant yellowwood tree together but I ended up doing this alone. It towered over me, and as I peered upwards I thought how many people must have lived and died through its long and solitary existence.

I walked back to the car and stopped behind some shrubbery, watching Nick. He had his head looking down, concentrating on something, although at first, I was not sure if he was taking a nap. As I neared the car, he looked up, shuffling uncomfortably and smiling in a strange way.

In the restaurant, we ate medium-rare steaks, which dominated our plates. They melted in our mouths and tasted heavenly. There seemed nothing more pleasurable than eating them while drinking a complimentary smoked South African Merlot.

Externally, everything looked picture-perfect. Here I was, eating delicious food in a stylish restaurant, drinking palatable wine, reminiscing and admiring my handsome boyfriend: seemingly a defining moment, despite my anxiousness.

Incidentally, I had eaten in this restaurant two years earlier with Phil, and I remembered a mixture of feelings then, at the end of that safari adventure holiday - happy emotions yet uncertainty about my future with him. My seven-year relationship with Phil had ended weeks later. Those feelings surfaced again, this time with Nick, but I sincerely hoped history was not about to repeat itself.

Within weeks of returning from South Africa, Nick worked late one night. I was left alone in the flat and my suspicions became intense. I reflected on different points of the holiday: walking alone to that tall yellowwood tree, Nick being quiet and the time he was looking down at something in the car as he waited for me. I thought about the nights when he slept as I lay awake, the timely 'food poisoning episode' and his coolness in the restaurant on our last day. Something had changed and something was wrong.

I paced the flat as I over-analysed; he had never been this late before. I walked back into the bedroom, looking around. I knew there was something in this room that I had to find. I walked over to the chest of drawers and, opening up the bottom drawer, I looked at Nick's clothes, carefully and neatly folded. I lifted his shirts to find a small piece of paper. I slowly picked it up, cautiously unfolded it, and saw a mobile phone number written in unfamiliar writing.

I put the piece of paper back in the drawer. After hesitating, I took it out again, and decided to call the number, but it went straight to voicemail with a message spoken in an Australian accent. Was this the reason why Nick had been so cool over the last few weeks? Had he met someone else?

Nick returned home late from 'work' that evening, and after a long argument, he ended the relationship. As I sat on his lap facing him, I asked him what was wrong and where he had been. He told me there was someone else – that their eyes had 'met' on a train. I felt sick inside.

It felt as if our 18-month relationship had lasted a lifetime already because we had done so much together. I had hoped that this relationship would have gone the distance – a real lifetime.

History had indeed repeated itself, at the same time of the year and in the same country, albeit with an unexplained ending - seemingly deceitful, brutal and heartless. This break up was different – like some kind of fatal 'head-on collision'. My perfect world stopped turning and my picture-perfect life was over, triggering a chain reaction of intense sadness and feelings of rejection, driving me beyond despair and opening up issues from my past that I can only say, spiralled out of control.

Each day that followed weighed down on me more, in terms of distress and loneliness. My world had fallen apart, and I began to slide down into a pit of deep quicksand – the more I tried to escape by clawing at its slippery sides, in sheer desperation to survive, the deeper I sank. Nick once promised he would 'never do this to me' – these were now just meaningless words.

Several days later, he moved out; our relationship had finished and his new relationship had started.

5

May 2002

Several days after the break up with Nick, I had an 'untimely' lesson observation at school (although they are never timely or warranted). Following the observation, I went into a 'mini- meltdown' and spilled the beans as the levels of stress seemed to be added, layer by layer. As the observer listened, he took pity on me, and tore up the observation form with a deliberate and over-exaggerated slowness – his sympathy erased the last hour of my life but, sadly, not the last few weeks.

I entered a period that I recall as the 'dark ages', despite the brighter days. I was a wounded deer struggling to survive.

As I drifted aimlessly into the middle of a colder and deeper ocean, I lost interest in everything and was swallowed up by a whirl-pool of self-pity. Something inside me had changed, and I became oblivious to most things going on around me – I just switched off to life.

Concerned friends invited me to restaurants, cinemas, bars, gym classes, art galleries, country walks and even weekend breaks away. A colleague invited me to go to Nice in the Côte d'Azur, and I did so, reluctantly. I had previously been there with Nick during our happier times and I remember, this time, looking down from the hostel's balcony at a sea of people walking in the street below, thinking to myself, 'How could one person in this world create so much devastation?'

My friends did everything to distract me from the reality of what was going on – deep down they cared, yet I seemed oblivious to their worries – I was beginning to drown in the middle of that cold and deep ocean.

I vaguely remember historic occasions later in that year: the Manchester Commonwealth Games and the Queen's Golden Jubilee Celebrations, and attended some of the events from both with different friends who had kindly invited me. Although I appreciated being

18

asked, I just sat there surrounded by thousands of people, watching with a glazed expression and, more importantly, not really wanting to be there – I just wanted to be with Nick.

After watching some of the competitions at the Commonwealth Games, I slowly returned to the car with Robbie (my best friend) - walking through a summer's evening downpour, and as I walked in the rain, I felt somewhat 'cleansed'.

Robbie was of similar age, had Jamaican heritage and he always saw the funny side of life. His genuine character with its exuberant warmth and friendliness was trying hard to pull me through this difficult time, perpetually trying to distract me from the reality of the situation, which must have been tiring for him.

Usually, we talked and laughed about everything: any subject or situation. We often saw the funnier side of life, even though we would often talk about current affairs: history, politics, religion, famous people, films and countries – he knew such a great deal of interesting information.

'How are you feeling about him now?' he asked. I knew Robbie cared about me but, deep down, he wanted to tell me something.

'It still feels raw. If you know something, though, please tell me. I think I just need to know.' Why was I stupidly encouraging pain? I was aware he kept in touch with Nick, but I did not mind; in fact, it was my strange way of staying in contact (which I actively encouraged). Secretly, I had hoped it was a channel of communication.

'Are you sure?' he asked, looking at me still concerned. At this point, we were ambling around the shops and feeling hungry after the day's events.

'Yes.'

'They are planning on moving to Australia later this year.'

How could life, that once seemed so perfectly sweet, turn so horribly sour?

6

June 2002

Now, it seemed my life was similar to a racehorse's: galloping at full speed and spraying mud everywhere, blinkered and aiming for that finishing line – nothing was going to get in my way, slow me down or stop me reaching that goal of a reconciliation with Nick.

Despite the cost and detriment to others (or myself), as each day passed, I became fixated, developing tunnel vision, believing anything would work to make this happen. I had entered a world of 'make-believe'.

An advert in the back pages of a free London newspaper caught my eye - 'Bring your ex-lover back.' 'What rubbish!' was my instant reaction. However, the advert played on my mind for several days and as my curiosity deepened, later that week, I made my first call. It was simply a tarot card reading, and I thought, 'What was the harm in that?'

With a vulnerable state of mind, I believed anything was possible. Within minutes, I was confiding in a random stranger who had a 'soothing telephone voice. She did a reading, saying, 'Reconciliation will happen, in time.' Maybe I was hearing what I needed to hear?

What did 'in time' actually mean? Was he going to come back in a few days, weeks, months, years or even in another life? I wanted to know, I wanted an answer, I wanted him back and needed to hear another reading telling me a definite answer to end the misery.

I made another call days later to a different advert but instead of being reassured and becoming more sceptical, I only became more gullible and addicted to tarot card readings carried out by people who had never even met me. I was increasingly curious, as if magic', could bring Nick back.

Rationally, I viewed people who performed spells or any type of magic as having 'no substance'. I simply did not believe anything about them and thought they would only create trouble, or at least create a troubled mind. However, as I browsed the Internet, I noticed black magic websites stating they could make 'anything' possible.

'Get your ex back today', 'Fast & powerful love spells', 'Love spells to bring back your ex', 'Ex-lover back guaranteed or your money back' – all phrased differently but meaning the same thing. Some of them stated, 'No payment required' or 'Pay when you see results', like some kind of experiment. The choice of adverts seemed endless but there was one message that came through clearly, 'anything is possible, anything at all and we can make this work for you – just for you'. It was as if it was a special message - just for me. In some ways, they paralleled horoscopes; it was personalised even though millions of people out there had the same star sign. Plainly ridiculous, but a strange kind of obsession was developing - I had taken this to a new and worrying level.

An invitation to dinner one evening with two good friends, Rima and Aram, proved to be hilarious (for them, at least).

Rima had been a good friend for several years and she had met Nick. She was small, bubbly, South Asian, around thirty years old and led a bohemian lifestyle. Aram was around the same age, tall and slim, half-Asian, unassuming with a gentle nature and had recently been through his own break-up.

'I'm sorry to hear about your situation, Aram.' His girlfriend had met someone else although there was a child involved. 'Are you ok?' I asked.

'Yeah, I'll be alright.' He smiled yet had a lost look in his eyes. I felt sorry for him, as he deserved to be happy and had so much to give; he was a great father too. He was now the shattered remains of the Aram I once knew. I smiled back and thought how difficult it must be, not just for the parents but also for the child who is caught up between them. It is said, children are more resilient than adults – that is debatable. However, you plan your life to have a child with someone and the relationship that you once thought was going to last forever is broken, against your will, must be even more difficult.

'Do you mind if I ask you something, Aram?'

'No, go ahead.'

I knew it was personal but I felt his break-up deserved more attention than mine. 'Will you still see your son?'

'Yes, of course. We are amicable and we are making arrangements for him to stay with me alternate weekends.'

'I hope it all works out.' The sudden realisation this could happen to anyone, at any time, made me even more aware I had been wallowing in self-pity.

'How are you coping?' Aram asked.

'It's been tough but I keep busy.'

'That's the best way, takes your mind off things', Aram agreed.

Before I had a chance to agree, I blurted out, 'I have been an idiot, though!'

They both froze in mid flow, looking at me with food-laden forks positioned halfway towards their open mouths, before they asked in unison, 'What have you done?' Rima smiled, while Aram looked at me, more concerned.

'I have done something, let's say … a bit weird.'

'What do you mean, a bit weird?' Aram asked, as he giggled yet still looking perplexed.

I started laughing nervously before answering. 'I have been asking people to cast magic spells for me!'

'No way!' Rima said, before breaking into a fit of giggles.

'Yes. I have been on the Internet and have become obsessed with magic spells to try to get Nick back.' We always had a good banter together, but this generated what I can only describe as canned laughter.

'You know, some websites have shopping carts, asking you to pay, so you can add spells to the cart.'

'It sounds like online shopping!' Aram affirmed.

'It does feel like that. You can buy as many spells as you want.' In some ways, it mirrored online gambling: you throw away your money hoping to win something – an ex-lover! I can understand why smoking, drinking, taking drugs and gambling are addictions but magic spells? 'Imagine going to rehab and saying, Hello, my name is Paul Wood and I am a black magic addict!' They laughed hysterically.

'Do you believe it works?' Aram asked curiously.

'It's not worked yet.' I started to laugh too.

'That's ridiculous', Rima added. Aram looked strangely at me probably thinking I had lost my mind.

'I spend a lot of time browsing the net to see if magic spells work, even during my free time at school – it is taking over my life!'

'Do you not think they are they just con artists?' Aram asked. I noticed a more concerned look on his face.

'You know what, they probably are. Do you think I have gone mad?' 'No, you just want him back', Rima replied, sympathetically.

'I have emailed spiritualists in different countries to cast bizarre spells and perform strange rituals.'

'What kind of strange rituals?' Rima asked, as we ate the tasty vegetarian food.

'Maybe I shouldn't tell you right now.'

'Go on, tell us.' Rima added.

'Sometimes, their strong accents are difficult to understand but one man said it would involve sacrificing an animal. Honestly, at one point, if it meant bringing Nick back, I would have gone down to a local farm and done it myself!'

'Oh my God!' Aram convulsed with laughter, nearly falling off his chair. I looked at two bodies distorted with laughter but knew I was falling deeper into this dangerous 'dark world', and on a serious note, I did not know how to escape.

'Well if there is a God, I bet he's not too happy with me!' I added.

There has to be some point when you need to let go, for your own sanity. This had become more about my past issues than just about the break-up with Nick. Having divorced parents, the bullying I experienced at school, having little contact with my mother in my early years of life and never really fitting in at school. I always felt that I was never really listened to a child by teachers, friends or, dare I say, parents, and that nobody really helped me. All I wanted was security, love, acceptance and normality – all deep-rooted issues. This was something complicated - psychological and disturbing, yet I was too scared to face any of it.

Rima glanced at me with a worrying look on her face.

'You know what, I phoned a woman from Nebraska and paid her two hundred dollars using my credit card.'

'Have you gone mad?' Aram asked.

'Yes!'

'What did she ask you to do?' Rima asked.

'Go to a park and stare into a pond.'

'I could have told you to do that and you could have paid me the two hundred dollars!' she replied. Her worried look changed into a strange smile.

'Wait for it. I sat by the pond at Streatham Common and stared into it for hours. I am sure people were walking past me and looking at me strangely.'

'They probably thought you had taken something?' Aram said.

I nodded. 'Then she told me to go home, sit on the kitchen floor, think of him, sit inside a circle of salt at night time, stare into candle flames in the darkness and chant.'

Total hysteria filled the room. At this point, I realised what I had done was completely ridiculous. 'When I sat there in that circle of salt and candles I couldn't stop laughing as I stared at the floor, then I started crying as it just hit me.' That day, the obsession ended – I was desperate for answers, but there seemed to be none. There was no reconciliation.

'Paul, you have totally cheered me up!' Aram stated.

'Well, at least I made someone laugh!'

We carried on eating and talked about other things, occasionally breaking into fits of giggles. At least I could see the funny side of it. As they talked, I thought about how desperate I had been. I had also asked members of my own family and friends to intervene, several times, in a desperate attempt to bring Nick back. I think it drove him further away, probably giving him the impression I had, indeed, totally lost my marbles. Maybe he and everyone I knew thought I had, but no matter what people thought of me, all I could still think about was that reconciliation.

My next phase was turning to faith.

In my own selfishness, I had contacted a friend and ex-colleague, who I had not seen for a while. She was a devout Christian. I now needed God to do his 'magic'. I was depending on God, depending on my friend, Sandy, for answers and needed her now, more than ever before. I truly believed her faith in God would work, yet still, there seemed to be no answer.

A male work colleague, who I had also confided in, invited me to an Alpha-Christian Group at a church hall in Peckham. He and his wife regularly attended the group but I had different intentions: this was just another desperate attempt to get Nick back.

At the prayer meeting, I looked at his wife.

'Do you mind if I ask what you are praying for?' She put her hand out, making a space of about two inches between her thumb and forefinger. I looked down at her hand, bemused.

'I just want something that big.'

'Sorry?' I began to smirk.

'It's just something small. God has made so many big things why can't he give me something that's small.' Surely, she was not praying about the size of her husband's penis?

Her husband smiled, understood my expression and quickly interrupted, 'She needs a new pancreas.'

'Oh ... right!' It was a good job I was in a church hall!

His wife was a diabetic and they both (and everyone else) prayed for her to have a pancreas transplant. I hoped her prayers were answered. I prayed for her too, and others who needed help, but of course I went there for selfish reasons. I was hoping praying would help me too. However, I did feel guilty for dabbling in black magic, and I began praying for forgiveness.

I looked around at everyone, deep in prayer as they wanted something important, yet I still kept on selfishly praying persistently for that reconciliation. I thought more about what she said, 'Something small.' Was wanting Nick back a small request, in the greater scheme of things? Was I being selfish praying for this? Should I have prayed to God to delete my microscopic brain cells containing memories of Nick? Brain cells are tiny but cause so much pain. Could God do that?

25

I looked around again at all these people who had turned to religion to help them cope with their problems, yet they also prayed for one another. I had nothing but respect for them.

During my last visit, I prayed for peace of mind.

As I tried to teach, I thought of Nick – the children's faces looked identical and on two or three occasions, I left my class to stand outside, staring at the floor, with tears welling up in my eyes, still not accepting the break up. I would go to the toilets at break or lunchtime nearly every day on my knees with my head over the toilet seat, begging God. It became a coping mechanism, and I kept on praying for that reconciliation.

As time passed, I realised that religion is not the equivalent of rubbing some rusty old magic lamp and waiting for a genie to appear in a puff of thick green smoke to grant three wishes.

Selfishly, I mistook praying as some form of a 'wish list' and was too self-absorbed to realise it was about developing a relationship with God when you want and need God only.

As I became calmer, I started to pray for peace – not just in a church, or at home, but everywhere. I started to believe God was around me all the time – not just within the confinements of a religious building.

I began to focus more on my job, which became my latest 'float' on that calmer ocean, often working longer hours and driving home in a daze, not knowing whether I was too exhausted or was still upset over Nick. I would often drive without remembering getting into the car. I was not only blocking out the world during the journeys I made to and from work, but in reality, it was the same routine each day and there seemed to be nothing in between.

Factually, the person I loved had left me for somebody else – a fact I was not yet facing. They were living in Australia together, in what seemed to be total harmony and getting on with their lives. I was here, hurting and still thinking about him.

I put them on a pedestal, like winners at the Olympic Games. It seemed a romantic notion; they had disappeared together into the sunset, and looking back, it all happened so quickly. Maybe, I was foolish or even naive, but I just did not see or want to believe there were any serious flaws in our relationship before it ended.

Somebody once told me that you could pay someone to 'finish' a person, and I woke up feeling very anxious in the early hours one morning as it rained heavily outside. I was shaking and sweating. Dressed only in jeans and a jumper and slippers, I left the flat, quickly driving out into the heavy rain in some zombie-like state, arriving in a poorly lit street.

I was angrier than I had ever felt before, upset and out of control as jealously raged through me like a forest fire – anger burning my insides. I shouted in the car, 'WHY THE FUCK DID HE DO THIS TO ME?'

I slowed down and drove around the dark streets about two or three miles away from my flat. The rain still poured down heavily with thunderous sounds pounding the metal bonnet. I could not see anything on the dark quiet street that wasn't far from an underground station.

I stopped the car, turned the engine off and rested my head on the headrest. I tried to calm myself down, breathing deeply as my heart pounded. There were men walking about, hoods up, looking suspicious, looking down at the ground. Were these people real or was I dreaming? One man, wearing a hooded top, walked slowly, looking through the window. I was too scared to look yet I wanted to stay here, in this evil place with my evil mind. Maybe he could 'finish' Nick? Was I in the scariest part of London or just the scariest part of my mind? Or having the scariest thoughts way too scary for anyone to think? To have someone you still love, murdered, and somebody out there could do that for me? I had the money and intention. I could pay him to kill Nick to end this pain.

I wonder if we are all 'potential murderers'? Would a parent want to kill someone who had sexually abused or murdered their child? Could anyone be driven to such desperate lengths if all their buttons were pressed? Could I?

The rain fell heavier and everything outside was blurry, including the thoughts in my mind. It was cold in the car and as I shivered, I turned the engine on, switched on the wipers and the heating. The hooded man had become a silhouette under the glowing yellow light of the streetlight in front of him.

He walked away as I watched his reflection grow smaller in the wing mirror. Who was the monster: him or me? Maybe, I had the completely wrong impression of him; maybe he was a drug dealer, maybe he wanted nothing at all, or was homeless. Was I stereotyping him just because of the colour of his skin?

I leaned back on the headrest remembering my innocent childhood and stared through the dark windscreen, the rain streaming down. Different images bounced around inside my troubled mind: memories of presents under the Christmas tree, two big long socks filled with shelled nuts, tangerines and small toys, dangling precariously over the 1970s tiled fireplace, while the wind whistled down the chimney causing the coal embers to glow bright orange.

Another memory of a family holiday in Devon, all of us packed inside a sixth-berth caravan on a rainy afternoon, huddled around a small portable television precariously balanced on a Formica coffee table with wobbly steel legs.

Another image of me perched on my bedroom window with my brother and cousin, watching fireworks through iced-over windows. Then another whisper of a memory of my younger brother and me, wearing shorts, as we precariously rode our new bicycles away from our proud smiling dad, who stood there, watching us in his oversized cardigan with his arms folded.

A tear suddenly rolled down my cheek, and I wished to relive those moments. I wanted to go back further in time and be inside my mother's womb and start life all over again.

I started the engine, slowly doing a U-turn in the continual downpour, and then drove back to my flat. It was raining like a monsoon. Was this a sign from God? Was he angry with me?

I put my foot down driving up the long steep hill that went on forever. A speeding camera suddenly flashed, but all I wanted was to be safe and away from this place. If I had gone through with this, my life would have changed forever. I got into bed shivering with damp hair and lay back on the pillow.

'What is happening to me?'

I looked at the other pillow and wished Nick was still there, next to me. I wanted him to hold me tight, just at this very moment, just to tell me he loved me. I longed to hear his words, 'I'm sorry.'

I loved him, yet I wanted him banished. Maybe, someone else out there had actually gone through with this. Maybe one of those men had carried out a 'job' for someone who was also going through pain. You hear about this on the news: jealous and uncontrollable rages affecting rationality. For a brief moment of my life, I wanted to murder someone. A plain and simple thought had entered my mind: 'If I can't have him, nobody can.'

I had to go to work the following day! How could I be normal after this? Maybe someone else had gone through a similar plan of action. How could they just get back into bed? How could they live with themselves after doing something like that?

I woke up the following morning, rushed into the living room and looked down from the window at my car, still parked in the same position as it rained. I never did receive that parking ticket. Did the events of last night really happen or was it just a horrible nightmare?

I had gone through all the possible stages of rejection and tried to think of all the reasons why it had happened, putting the blame on others or my parents divorcing when I was young. I even used the excuse of my upbringing as a way of explaining my recent irrational behaviour. Maybe, there is an element of truth in that – we are all a product of our upbringing. At times, I even tried to think my ex-partner had died, as it seemed to be a way of coping with the pain and dealing with this situation. Rejection seemed worse than death, because he still existed. I thought I would never get over this break-up.

Most people go through the stages of denial, depression, anger and acceptance after any type of trauma. Everyone goes through these stages at a different pace, and not necessarily in that order; when you feel trapped at any of these stages, in my opinion, it is time to seek professional help. I was only with him for 18 months out of the 35

29

years of my existence, so why was this thin slice of life affecting everything?

Slowly, the pain healed, and for the rest of that year, I started to develop a better and healthier mentality. I would sometimes give money to homeless people or go into a shop and buy them food and hot drinks and walk back to them, although, sometimes, they had disappeared.

One warm afternoon, I walked past an old woman crouched over a big black dog lying down on a street in Battersea. I made tentative steps towards her and wondered if I should help her. Her dog looked like it had died but I did not have the heart to tell her. Through her tears, she begged me to help her.

As she continued crying, she tried to direct me to the nearest veterinary practice. She had also lost something precious: an animal that had probably given her years of unconditional love.

She said it was a 'ten-minute walk up Lavender Hill'. I usually only went to Battersea to shop, not to rescue dead dogs! However, I carried the dog for what seemed like an eternity, which was back-breaking, yet I persevered and made it to the veterinary practice as quickly as I could. She must have thought I was some kind of power-lifter on steroids – she was desperate and this dog was her only companion.

The dog had drooled all over me, was limp and seemed to get heavier with every step I took, especially in the last few minutes.

I was unaware of the other people walking past me in the street as I tried to reposition the dog over my shoulder. I eventually stumbled sideways through the small door, arriving at the veterinary practice. I gently laid the dog down in the middle of the floor, straining my back as I did so, within a circle of seated people and their pets. I tried to regain my breath while every pair of eyes, including all the dogs and cats in boxes, seemed to be staring at me.

A concerned veterinary nurse hurried over, inundating me with questions. Suddenly, the dog sprang to life, nearly knocking her owner to the floor. The frail old woman shrieked with delight as she put her arms around the dog and kneeled down as it fastidiously licked her face.

That was a well-deserved and rather emotional reconciliation. The dog had just fainted in the heat of the summer sun and as the old woman cried (with happiness) everybody clapped. I slowly stood up, looked down at her and the circle of happy people and their panting pets and discreetly left.

I carried on doing charitable tasks and in some ways, it made me feel good inside and less guilty and selfish about my behaviour in recent months. I just wanted to be a kinder and selfless person, to wipe the slate clean and to see the good in everybody. I had to forgive Nick and erase the guilt; it was my way of 'starting over'.

Robbie once said, 'Kind words, kind thoughts, kind deeds.' I tried to hold on to those words.

One Saturday afternoon, late June 2002, I sat in a cafe opposite Harrods, with my Christian friend Sandy. She was older than me, and had a small frame and red hair, cut neatly into a bob. She had a softly spoken friendly voice with a suggestion of a Northern accent and was dry-humoured and witty, often looking at life from the same angle as me.

Again, it was unusually warm for this time of year.

An old car had broken down on the corner of the street opposite the cafe, quickly creating congested traffic on the Brompton Road. People just carried on with their own lives, walking past the car and choosing not to get involved, and other people around me in the open-air cafe carried on talking, trying to ignore it, or maybe they just did not notice.

'I am going to help them!'

'What?' I noticed apprehension in her eyes.

'I won't be too long!'

My cup clinked as I quickly placed it back on the saucer. I left the cafe and ran over to the car, which was the biggest, oldest and the heaviest Mercedes in the world! I offered to help the distressed Middle Eastern elderly couple and pushed their car to a safer place, and after doing so, I slowly walked back to the cafe.

31

'You had better call me an ambulance!' I said jokingly as I entered, gasping for breath.

'What?'

'That was like trying to push a steamroller with its brakes locked!'
She looked alarmed, getting out of her seat immediately.

'Well, maybe a long sit-down and several cups of tea will help!'
She laughed sympathetically.

'That was a kind thing to do.'

'From now on, it is time to be bloody selfish!'

She laughed again shaking her head. 'Would you like another cuppa?'

7

July 2002

A night out watching the musical *Mama Mia* with work colleagues in Central London, weeks after we had broken up, triggered thoughts of Nick. At the end of the musical, 'The winner takes it all' was sung by the entire cast and everyone in the audience as the two main characters walked off stage into a mock sunset scene wearing backpacks to start new lives. As everyone in the audience applauded at the final scene, I sat quietly and thought of Nick and his new partner, leaving England, excited about their prosperous future in Australia – they were the 'winners who took it all' and I was the 'loser who had to fall.'

I thought about Nick too, on the last day of term, sitting alone on the steps of a fire escape at school, looking down over a crowd of excited teachers and thinking many of them would be going on holiday with their respective partners or about to enjoy their six weeks of freedom.

Students traditionally left at lunchtime and the teachers remained behind for a free buffet and drinks, usually outside on the forecourt. The teachers would eat, drink, laugh and switch off, becoming 'human' again. The school principal talked, thanking everyone for their hard work over the year. Some teachers left the school, received promotion, went on maternity leave or retired and recited their respective leaving speeches.

All I knew at the present moment was that the six-week summer holiday would feel like a long time without the distraction of work; this would give me time to think, take stock and allow those wounds to heal.

It was hard and, despite frequent reminders of Nick, I had to embrace my single life. For the remainder of the year, I slowly started to get my life back. I tried to purposely replace whispers of painful memories with fond ones that we once shared, but much of what I remember of 2002 is still a blur.

Once the summer holidays had started, I spent a few days decluttering and cleaning my flat, and saw friends before leaving London, in order to spend the rest of the summer holidays with my dad.

I was grateful to have someone to rely on for support and company for what I thought would be a lonely period; I did not return to London until the beginning of September.

8

September 2002

I felt refreshed and ploughed into work straight away, putting my heart and soul into my job, often working late; and once the dark nights started drawing in, I did not see much daylight during the working week.

I was quickly promoted to a junior management position. I also joined a local gym, acquired a personal trainer, attended various fitness classes and started doing some DIY to my flat at the weekends.

I saw more of my friends and, gradually, started appreciating my own company again; I even acquired a kitten (from my sister-in-law), who I named 'Jack'.

I felt happier and strong enough for some professional advice – a way of becoming healthier. A brain needs looking after, just like any other organ.

Taking brave steps each Friday, at around 5 p.m., I travelled to Seven Sisters in North London to see a counsellor. I despised the long and lonely journey and this part of London seemed bleak and soulless – people rushing everywhere, new faces each time – but I found solace once I arrived and started talking to my counsellor.

We addressed the issues of rejection and the reasons why I held on to love: maybe it was because my mother left my father when I was a young child. Going through my childhood was painful but, after two or three visits, I gradually gained some comfort from these conversations and came to terms with my experiences. However, on the odd occasion, I would leave feeling raw.

As each week passed, I began to feel more aware of who I was and how my behaviour and emotions were affected by my challenging childhood experiences. First there was having divorced parents at a young age and all the lies I told my friends to hide the shame. Then rejection from my mother and at school, years of bullying; being brought up just by my father and being in denial about my sexuality

35

throughout school life all added to the load. And, finally, playing a 'mother' role to my younger brother and not realising the harm it was doing to me – a heavy burden for any child.

My mother had left when I was six years old and my parents had divorced two years later. As I grew older, I remember cleaning the house, especially at the weekends, lying to friends at school by saying that my auntie was really my mother – desperately wanting the 'normal family life' all my friends seemed to have and, I thought, everybody else. It was difficult to keep lying about it but it made my home life seem more acceptable (to me and everyone else) – it was a blanket of disguise.

I detached myself from reality and lost my identity as a child, as a boy; at times, I would be angry at myself, the situation I was faced with and, regrettably, at my dad for putting me in this situation. It was never his fault but sometimes I 'blamed' him, not directly but in a pent-up, frustrated way; really, I should have been grateful and supported him, in the best way a child could.

I was too young to understand and appreciate how hard it must have been for him although I was aware that my family was 'different'. My dad wanted to bring up my younger brother and me, and, naturally, he wanted us to be happy.

As the counsellor listened, it felt as if I was opening up the book of my life that had been sealed and covered in dust. As difficult as these sessions were, it felt liberating to tell him how I was feeling, and, in some ways, I felt nurtured by him and I realised these sessions helped me to 'grow' and move forward.

The autumn term passed quickly and, again, I left London for the Christmas break. I always considered Christmas a 'special' time, but it was more important now, to be with my family.

Since the break-up, it was my first Christmas without Nick and maybe his first Christmas with his new partner. Wherever they were, they had each other and I believe, at this point, they had moved to Australia.

Nothing could ever take away the love I once had for Nick: that was something I had to hold on to. Now, I just smiled more when I thought of him and sincerely hoped he was happy too. I am sure he had reasons for ending our relationship and I am certain he had his own difficulties to face, as we all do. Finally, I had arrived at a stage of acceptance, which had been an important journey.

Whatever had caused the break-up of my parents' marriage, I never blamed either of them; what was important now was having better relationships with my mother and father in different and fulfilling ways.

I started re-establishing contact with my mother, building a stronger and happier relationship with her. In some ways, I wanted to make up for lost time, although I had seen her once a week as a young teenager.

I was honest with my dad and told him that I had decided to start seeing my mother again, at the same time assuring him that I loved him. Seeing my mother would never change how I felt about him. My dad was my 'silent protector', my friend and importantly, my father; regrettably, I never told him he was my role model.

He kindly accepted my decision and appreciated my honesty. Nobody would ever replace my dad. My mum and dad were separate people, with separate lives and totally different personalities. I had to respect that, and now, the situation worked for me – if only I had realised and appreciated that when I was younger, maybe I would have been a different person today, dealing with my own difficulties, particularly relationships that I was in, very differently.

Christmas was enjoyable and relaxing but as usual, all too short. My career was still going well and my salary had recently improved. I thought more about all the good aspects of life – owning a flat in London, driving a sports car, having a secure career and reliable friends – and I was grateful.

I had almost completed four productive years at this school and the only setback during my period of growth was going through a difficult break-up; but now, that was in the past. Importantly, work had provided me with a 'distraction' and stability, helping to carry me through a difficult period.

In the smoking room at my school, several work colleagues would often be in there during the breaks. One time, I walked in to face a group of people smoking and looking up at a wall- mounted TV showing Kylie Minogue's latest music video, *Love at first sight* (a combination of Kylie and her dancers moving robotically in front of futuristic backdrops) – she was at the height of her fame.

Nobody noticed as I entered – they were all transfixed by the TV screen, while puffing on their cigarettes in the little time they had.

I glanced over at a tattered and torn paper lying on the table, advertising teaching jobs. I picked it up and perched myself on the edge of the seat next to the table, hurriedly skimming through most of the adverts in the science section in the precious minutes remaining before my next lesson started.

The room smelled strongly of fresh cigarette smoke – maybe the smokers here had become immune to it. I looked at the overseas section on back of the paper, quickly scanning over a page advertising teaching jobs in different countries: Spain, Japan, Brussels and many in the Middle East offering tax-free salaries. I was tempted to apply, especially now I had no ties; I could earn considerably more teaching there for a year or two of my life and it would allow me to set some money aside. One advert in particular caught my attention: a company recruiting British teachers to work in America, called VIF (Visiting International Faculty), and as I read the advertisement quickly, the school bell suddenly rang.

I quickly put the paper down and walked back to my laboratory, thinking of those job adverts, particularly the American one, while clumsily bumping into students in the crowded narrowed corridor on my way to take the afternoon register. Teaching abroad had a distinct appeal.

It was just another ordinary afternoon of teaching, but during the quieter moments, especially when my students were concentrating on answering questions, I gazed through the window and thought more about that advert for jobs in America.

I thought about my first visit to the US and how exciting it had felt; New York and Boston during my days at the polytechnic. I had also been to New York, years later, for a long weekend with Phil - and I remembered feeling 'British' and feeling proud of my country, mainly because Americans adored the British accent and seemed to take more of an interest.

It was the end of the school day. I went through my usual routine of tidying my desk and checking through my teacher planner for the following day's lessons, placing my chair under my desk and collecting my jacket and bag from the prep room. Before going home, I hesitated, thinking about the job advert. I walked down the empty corridors into the smoking room, now devoid of teachers and clouds of smoke, to see the coffee-stained paper lying on the table in exactly the same position.

I walked over and picked up the paper, looking for the American job advert again. I put the paper back on the table and headed for the door but then stopped, and shook my head indecisively. I turned around and picked up the paper again, tore out the advert, placed it in my wallet and went home.

I was afloat in the middle of that calm ocean.

It was early March 2003, not long before school broke up for Easter, and it had been almost one year since my relationship with Nick had ended.

I was a 'social smoker' (not that smoking is sociable for other non-smokers around you) and only smoked if the other person offered me a cigarette; but on that particular day, I decided to go and take another visit to the smokers' room at lunchtime to meet fellow teachers who were usually more fun to be with. I became good friends with a female work colleague called Halise, who, ironically, was Australian with Turkish ancestry. She too, had been through a recent break-up. Other work colleagues had introduced us at staff parties and we clicked immediately, always bantering in the staffroom or if we passed each in other in the corridor.

She often cracked jokes and was personable, and I warmed to her quickly. We shared a similar sense of humour: wit, sarcasm and often, mindless fun. I also had the opportunity of meeting her English ex-boyfriend, who seemed quieter and pleasant. I started to go down to the smoking room more regularly, just to enjoy her company, and we

39

became good friends.

Halise had originally planned to go on a tour of Italy for two weeks with her fiancé during the Easter holidays, meticulously planning every aspect of the holiday: booking the flights, all of the interconnecting train journeys between Italian cities and the accommodation in the different places they were staying. They had also planned their engagement, but he had broken it off recently, which must have been awful for her.

She was petite, 27 years old, and had olive skin, green eyes and a wide bright smile. She dressed fashionably and oozed confidence, a little feisty at times, but in a friendly and funny way. Her personality and warmth reminded me of people back in Northern England. Moreover, she was genuine and she was devoted to her ex-fiancé but deep down, even though she kept her emotions hidden, I sensed she was secretly devastated when they had broken up.

I had confided in her at work when my relationship ended as she was a good listener and had always been supportive. Regrettably, she could not cancel any of the arrangements of their Italian tour as almost every aspect of it had been booked online and as most of the companies would not offer her any refunds, she was uncertain what to do.

Suddenly, I faced a new situation. Out of the blue she asked me go with her, to replace her ex-fiancé, one week before departure!

I was now in this predicament. Should I accept or politely decline her extremely generous offer? She said, 'just pay for my flight', which I did. I partly felt guilty, not because I was going on a tour of Italy on a shoestring but because she was meant to have had the 'romantic' trip of a lifetime with her fiancé.

However, I had to make this decision quickly, otherwise I would have missed this unique opportunity.

I had just a few days before we were due to leave, and this was my first real experience of being a back-packer – it was not a beach holiday, I did not need an over-sized suitcase and it was spontaneous and exciting. Sometimes, I think that is the best way.

After school, I bought a backpack from a local market, some trainers and checked my passport was still valid.

Looking back, our new friendship and this unexpected Italian adventure could only be described as destiny carving my future.

9

April 2003

Early Saturday morning, we travelled by train to Gatwick Airport, to catch our flight to Milan – my first visit to Italy.

Once we had arrived, we kept a low profile for the rest of the day —window shopping and drinking coffee at different cafes dotted around the city centre.

Then, we made our way to the rather small and luxurious hotel in central Milan to have a power nap, as we still felt tired. Following a recharge, we walked to a bar, where we drank Kahlua and Coke and ate authentic-looking pizza.

'I've never seen pizza with just a ring of cheese in the middle, before', Halise confessed.

'Just-a-like-a Mama used to make.' I tried to imitate an Italian accent.

'I think originally, they sold it as street food.'

'I heard that too and I prefer cheese in the middle to be honest. I think we have too much cheese on ours, back home.'

'That's probably why people eat it with salad to make themselves feel healthy', Halise said. The pizza was laden with olives, artichokes, Italian cured meats, piled high with fresh rocket leaves and drizzled in olive oil – quite an unusual sight. We also ordered a bottle of red wine.

Following a good night's sleep, we felt refreshed. We wandered around Milan, sauntering past the Duomo, which gleamed in the sunlight, and then entered the Galleria Vittorio Emanuele II – the polished tiled floor inside this 19th-century shopping mall reflected the sunlight shining through its arching glass roof, illuminating the magnificent space inside.

'I feel important just being in here, do you?', I asked.

'Yeah, it's just so…luxurious.' Halise looked pleased with herself, as we strolled around expensive designer shops.

We stopped for a coffee before walking to the Santa Maria delle

Grazie (a church and Dominican convent called the Holy Mary of Grace), to look at Leonardo da Vinci's *Last Supper* - an entrancing painting of Jesus surrounded by his disciples.

We went window shopping again, and then made our way back to our hotel to pick up our luggage, check out and board a train to our next destination.

Venice looked like a picture postcard and the whole atmosphere had a romantic feel to it but after several hours, much of Venice looked the same.

We then bought return tickets to Verona, as Halise wanted see Juliet's Balcony. Touching the right breast of the golden statue of Juliet was supposed to bring you luck in love! Believe me, because of my feelings about past beliefs in insane superstitions I would have cupped both breasts all day, although the other tourists, and possibly the local polizia, would not have been impressed. However, we both touched the right breast of Juliet, regardless, then ambled over to Juliet's Balcony, admiring the hundreds of messages of love written on multicoloured 'sticky' notes – a whole wall of people in love from all different parts of the world!

There were crowds of people having their photographs taken, looking down from the balcony with their respective partners or holding their arms wide apart to express their love, which had relevance for both of us.

Romeo and Juliet: the most famous and tragic love story of all time but still, it felt poignant being there, maybe more for Halise – she looked reflective and I thought about her sadness.

After looking at the pink Roman amphitheatre, we hopped on a passing bus heading back to central Verona and caught a train back to Venice. That evening, at a local restaurant, we ordered lobster, staring at it for several minutes without knowing what to do.

'Where do I start?' Halise asked.

'It feels like some kind of weird dissection!' I commented.

'I wish you had not said that but I'll tell you what?' she said.

'What?' I asked, as Halise started tapping hard with her fork on its shell. 'It's a mission trying to eat this and it's expensive too!' she

43

gaffed.

After we had eaten, we walked around the narrow, cobbled streets in the late hours of the night, stopping for coffee in the San Marco area.

Even though Venice is a picturesque city for the ultimate romantic experience, we stayed at a campsite. I was certain Halise had been looking forward to this part of the trip and I glanced at her, thinking about how she must have wanted to share this moment with her fiancé.

The following day, we travelled further south by train, taking us to our next destination: Florence.

We walked up a steep hill to reach the campsite on a very warm afternoon, stopping several times to recover from the rigorous climb, drinking copious amounts of water to quench our thirst. Once we arrived at the top, we admired a clear view of Florence – a characteristic vista of rusty-brown terracotta roofs and a myriad of medieval streets.

The city appeared calm, and I wanted to venture down every single cobbled street, its captivating beauty reminding me of an enchanted fairy-tale.

Florence is one of the most beautiful cities I have visited and as the sun set over the city, the roofs were transformed into numerous seductive colours – rich shades of dark pinks to deep reds and browns – the scene was mesmerising.

After absorbing the magnificent views, we experienced a night of luxury, sleeping in a small plastic orange pod at the campsite!

In the morning, we left our bags in the pod and locked the door, and proceeded cautiously down the steep hill, which was more suited to abseiling than walking! I thought God knows how I would climb this again, especially after a few drinks!

However, it was a pleasant walk into Florence, a city with so much culture and history, containing many art galleries and museums, and I wanted to explore as much as possible in the short time we had.

I appreciated the architecture of the Renaissance buildings and looked around in complete amazement, marvelling at the sights of the Galleria dell' Accademia (Gallery of the Academy of Florence), the

Piazza della Signoria (the most famous square in Florence), the Duomo, followed by the Palazzo Pitti (the Pitti Palace), appearing as one huge collage of Renaissance art and all looking incredible in the orange sunset.

Feeling ravenous after our self-designed tour, pasta was on the menu again, and we drank one too many rather large gin and tonics, jumped into a taxi and went back to the campsite. This was a travelling experience, and I felt excited despite waking up the following morning with a dull headache from the mix of strong gin and loud voices in the neighbouring tent. Halise, who was still asleep with her mouth wide open, groaned as she curled up into a foetal position cocooned inside a sleeping bag.

I decided to shower and change, leaving her to sleep, and as I made my way to the shower block, I stopped at the viewpoint again that overlooked the magical city below, so unspoilt and otherworldly. I thought about Halise sleeping so peacefully. She must have been going through her own pain and I had not appreciated how difficult this must have been for her.

I felt reflective and continued admiring the views of Florence which looked stunning and serene, glowing in the morning sun. I could have stood there all day, as it gave me a sense of peace, making me reflect not just about the holiday, but life in general. My heart slowed down. I had made headway, and at that moment, as I smiled and looked around in all directions, I could not imagine being happier. I felt as if I had been a fly stuck in a spider's web for a long time, finally shaking free and escaping the trap – I was moving on.

I leaned against a small stone wall and closed my eyes. The air was fresh and I started to relax, the wall gently cushioning my body. This special place seemed perfect. Despite being alone, I felt safe as a feeling of calm filled my body and mind. I opened my eyes again. The temperature felt comfortable, and as I looked at my surroundings – buildings, trees, the horizon, a bright blue sky – I felt a stillness in the air and peace surrounding me. It felt like an epiphany and I felt in control, that I was in touch with my true self, more than I had ever had been before. I closed my eyes again and realised I did not need to depend on anyone, and I was letting go; I was conscious of each relaxing breath, and of the dwindling emotional fire and smoke that on each exhalation, gently drifted away and left my body and mind.

This journey to Italy had reignited my self-confidence and my spirituality – I had connected with my surroundings and now I had all the tools I needed to connect with myself, to my own heart. I was thinking more positively and said quietly to myself, 'I can get through this.' I focused on a better version of myself; having accepted my mistakes, and I was convinced life's experiences had made me stronger, and I had made the right choice coming to Italy – a place in which to grow and appreciate life.

I felt an inner calm and my eyes and heart were opening up to the possibilities coming my way. New thoughts entered my head about the teaching job in America. I decided that going there would be the best solution for me.

My experience in Italy had resulted in personal growth and I felt the need to work and live in another country; to experience being on my own and having to adapt, improve and survive. I needed to find myself, in another place. Maybe America was that place.

Following my moments of reflection, I walked over to a cafe, and bought cappuccinos and Danish pastries for breakfast. Feeling peaceful, I calmly walked back, stopping to admire the panoramic view one final time – the rooftops glowed intensely with the warmth of the sun. When I arrived back at the pod with the breakfast, Halise was getting ready and after packing our things, and eating, we left Florence.

The tower of Pisa seemed to defy the laws of gravity. The area was busy with tourists, despite being early in the day. A few people thought it was 'cool' to have photographs taken of them pretending to 'push over' the tower, and this trend spread quickly among the crowd. It was warm already as we sat on the grass opposite the tower and drank some water. Halise gave me yet another one of her cigarettes.

'I owe you at least ten packs!' I said.

'At least!' she laughed. 'Don't worry, it keeps me healthier if you smoke some too.' As we walked slowly towards the train station, Halise remained solemn.

'Are you okay?'

She paused before answering, 'Yeah, thanks for asking.'

'I was just thinking of you.'

'Hey, come on, we have both been through a difficult time.'

'Yeah, but you were engaged – it's different.'

We stopped walking and faced each other as she lit two more cigarettes and we sat down on a small stone wall.

'You were too!'

'Yeah, I know, but this was meant to be your holiday, your adventure, Halise.'

'It's our holiday now and our adventure', she affirmed. 'You know what, I can't understand how some people move on so quickly. It takes me time to get over someone, even when I have finished with them!'

'I know what you mean but I guess everyone is different.'

She looked at me, expressionless before continuing.

'I know you are thinking things were different for both of us, but remember, everyone is different and everyone deals with break-ups in their own way. Maybe Nick's love faded a long time before you realised or maybe he was incapable of committing. It's difficult to say as I didn't know him.'

I remembered South Africa and Nick's 'quietness', his 'bad stomach' and the moments before and after the 'yellowwood tree episode'. Maybe Nick and his partner were in contact at that point or maybe he knew our relationship was over – not that it mattered now.

'You said there was a history of him moving on from one person to the next. Maybe there is something in that? Maybe it is more about him than you. Perhaps his new relationship will not last either. Some people just can't deal with being single', Halise explained.

'Maybe you're right.'

I shrugged my shoulders, as there seemed no sense in anything that had happened; however, what she was saying felt comforting and I could not have processed this several months ago.

'Sometimes it is still hard to accept what happened, even after all this time.'

47

'No relationship break-up is easy.'

'If this other person was the 'love of his life', fair enough, but to be in a chain of 'rejected' people saddened me. It made me feel worthless.' I felt upset as I tried to explain, and she picked up on it.

'Just stop thinking about that now. Maybe, it's not about you. I know you, and I know what you want. You want 'commitment', and there is nothing wrong with that. Look, you are a good person, remember that.'

'Why do you always seem to say the right things? This is just what I need to hear. Look, he was just young, and it was fun while it lasted, maybe more from his point of view, but I loved him. I was young once, and I used to look at life differently – that's what it is all about. And you know what, I am not asking for any compliments, but it is kind of you to say that.'

'I am just trying to help you understand the situation.'

'I know you are. What about you?'

'What about me?' she asked.

'You know what I mean!'

She looked down, and put out her cigarette.

'I don't know. It feels quite … raw. Some days, it does not stop going around in my head. Like, it is out of control. Some days, I try not to think of him and I hate myself when I do but I cannot help it. Sometimes, I still wake up, thinking of him and it is just … so annoying. I want to forget about him but hate that too, as it makes me feel guilty that I want to forget about him. I sometimes think, what did I do wrong? How did this happen? Why am I here?'

'Thanks a lot!'

'You know what I mean! It feels surreal as I never expected to be here without him when we arranged it. I thought, this will be the ultimate travelling experience with someone I love, and I couldn't wait to share these experiences. We talked about it so much together. I thought we were both looking forward to this holiday of a lifetime.'

'Well, you could have booked a nicer tent', I said. We both laughed, and it seemed to clear the air.

'You cheeky … bastard! It was intimate, wasn't it?' We laughed again. 'Life is cruel sometimes, even for the best of us. I fucking hate men! I might become a lesbian!'

'Me too!'

We both laughed for several minutes until it hurt our sides. Once I had calmed down, I looked at her and smiled. 'I'm sure being a lesbian is no easier.'

'You're right.'

'How do you know?'

'Oh, shut-up! You know what? We don't piss each other off.'

'I think it's a sign of a good friendship', Halise smiled back as we walked.

'I think no matter what type of relationship you are in these days, the grass is greener, especially, once you are over thirty-five and when you are gay, you are definitely on the shelf!'

'I don't understand it?'

'Believe me, the number of gay websites I have been on, asking how old you are is the first question.'

'But, you look good for your age.'

'You cheeky … bitch!' She laughed.

'You know what I mean. Ri–di–cu–lous!' she exclaimed in a kind of slow, Russian-sounding accent. 'What do guys want?'

'You need to ask Stephen Hawking that question. I really don't know the answer.' We giggled again. 'Maybe I am destined for the single life, like my dad, but you know something, he seems happy enough. Maybe I should take a leaf out of his book?'

'Maybe you should!'

'I have been thinking, lately, I don't want to be in a relationship. I am too vulnerable. Thanks for asking me to come to Italy. You know what, this trip has been amazing, and it is helping me to think.'

'Think about what?' We stopped walking again.

'Working abroad.'

'Where?'

'America.'

'Really?'

'I saw an advert before Easter. I know it's a big decision but I have been thinking a lot.'

'It might be a good time to go now you are single.'

'Why?'

'See it as a journey.'

'A journey?'

'Yeah, a journey in yourself and by yourself.'

'I like the sound of that. Does it sound irrational?' I asked.

'No. Making that decision just after breaking up would have been irrational.'

'I travelled to America with a friend once, for a month, and loved it. Coming here has also made me think I would like to travel there again but the thought of going alone scares me a bit.'

'It might make you stronger', she explained. 'Travelling sets you free, if you know what I mean?'

'I know what you mean. That is how coming to Italy has made me feel – like, I am not answerable to anyone and, free, like a flying bird. When I woke up in Florence, I liked the feeling of being able to do what I wanted, when I wanted.'

'I think that is why I came to the UK. Everything is new and does not give you the chance to think about yourself for a while, although you get to know yourself because you are doing something major, something important by yourself. It's a big step and it might help you find out more about yourself.'

'Yeah, it might.'

'Well, you would have the best of both worlds: you could teach and travel. You could explore America and explore your mind!'

'I understand. You know, when I was looking at down at Florence from the top of the hill, I wanted to go off on my own to explore.'

'America could be an adventure?'

'You know, it is hard being in a relationship too. Sometimes it makes you feel secure but it ties your wings. Anyway, forget about me, how are you feeling? If you want to talk, I am here for you, okay?' I said. 'I mean that!' It was some time before she answered.

'I just feel numb about it all, I guess and in disbelief sometimes. The weird thing is, it has not sunk in yet, even though it happened. I am not sure if there is somebody else, but I don't think there is. That is the confusing bit. I just do not know. He seems happy.'

'It must have been difficult for you Halise, especially coming here.

I have been selfish thinking about my own emotions. I would have found it tough coming here with someone else if this holiday was originally planned for Nick and me. I am sorry I have been going on about myself.'

'Stop apologising. It is not necessary, but thank you, and it has been quite nice not thinking about my own problems, for a change. I am very happy you came with me.'

She stopped and hugged me. I put my arms around her too and in a broken voice, she said, 'Maybe, I am a complete bitch or something?'

A distinct tear rolled down her cheek. It was the first time I had seen her cry. 'It must have been hard for you too. Maybe, you are stronger than you realise?' I held her small shoulders and looked deep into her eyes.

'Hey, come on, we have each other, right now, and we need to enjoy this holiday. Forget about life and forget about men – they are all bastards!'

She smiled and sniggered as I let go of her shoulders but I felt she needed protection despite her inner strength.

'Eh, come on bitch!' I said. We both giggled. 'Hey, you are hardly a bitch. He's a fucking idiot.' I tried to say it in an Australian accent sounding more like a drunken cockney but at least it raised a smile from her.

'We have both come out of broken relationships, so let's have fun', Halise added. I smiled and looked at her as we approached the train station.

We arrived back in Florence late afternoon and walked back to the Galleria dell'Accademia to look at Michelangelo's famous statue of *David*. After standing in a short queue, we entered the room where the stunning statue was displayed: the white spotlights subtlety emphasised his athletic build and the smooth white marble.

Around the Piazza della Repubblica area, we noticed the high prices of the beautiful designer clothing and I did not have the money to even buy a pair of designer shoelaces!

After finding a place to eat meatballs and bread, we drank cheap red wine as we chatted more about relationships, leaving around 10 p.m. to get another early night, even though we talked until late.

The following morning, we boarded a busy train and used our backpacks as seats, positioning ourselves near the internal doors at the end of the train carriage, thereby benefiting from a cool breeze each time they opened and closed. A woman sat next to us on the floor and smiled as she leaned against her small rucksack.

'Where are you heading?' she confidently asked.

In unison, we answered, 'Rome!'

She giggled and shook hands. 'I'm Angel! I am from Texas, and, yes, I am not fat!' She laughed loudly.

We looked at each other with glazed expressions. 'Where are you guys from?'

Halise replied, 'We live in London. We are travelling around Italy for two weeks.'

I butted in, 'Yes, our Italian adventure.'

'Sounds awesome.' Despite her exuberance, she seemed to have a calming nature. Angel carried on talking. 'You guys are lucky having Europe on your doorstep.'

'So, are you here for long?' Halise asked her.

'I'm visiting a friend for two weeks but should be studying for exams. I thought, what the hell!'

'Are you at college?' I asked.

'Yeah. I am reading Italian. I know, a thin Texan studying Italian!' She laughed again. We smiled at her and looked at each other.

'Where are you studying?' Halise asked.

'Chapel Hill University?'

'Where is that?'

'North Carolina.' Halise looked at me and smiled.

'Why there, if you are from Texas?' I asked.

'Well. I had a few problems back home and wanted to get away. They also did not offer the course I wanted in Texas, so I decided to study out of state. Have you been there?'

'No', I replied. 'What is like there?'

'Chapel Hill or North Carolina?' she asked.

'Both?'

'Chapel Hill is nice and the course is great. I love it there.'

'What about North Carolina?'

'It's a beautiful state. Very peaceful and the people are friendly. There's a lot of cotton fields and mountains, if you like that kind of thing?' She had a satisfied smile.

'To be honest, I have seen a job I might apply for in America and one place I could work is North Carolina.'

'Where are the other places?'

'Atlanta, Utah, Virginia and South Carolina.'

'You should choose North Carolina,' she laughed.

'Thanks, I will think about it.

Halise and I were tiring and I nodded off, waking up later with a sore neck. Halise was still asleep, but Angel was wide-awake reading her book and as she looked at me, she smiled. The train was slowing down so I woke Halise up.

We had arrived in Rome. I am glad we met Angel and had that short conversation with her and I kept thinking about the last thing she said: 'You should choose North Carolina.'

After saying goodbye to Angel, we walked to the hostel located near Termini station and the receptionist told us we were sharing a room with eight others.

10

Inside the room, two men looked unconscious, sleeping with arms dangling over the edge of the beds with their mouths wide open. We could smell a faint whiff of marijuana, and I assumed they were stoned. One man sleeping had a small radio next to him, quietly playing 'Broken Wings' by Mr. Mister and I wondered how many songs, plays and films throughout history are about someone with a broken heart. I suddenly thought of the conversation I had with Halise in Pisa about wings and the feelings of flying high above the city of Florence. I wanted my wings to be fixed, so I could fly.

'Time to hit the streets of, Rome!' Halise spoke, excitedly, as I looked at her.

'I need intravenous caffeine and one of your ciggies?' I smiled cheekily as I asked.

Most of the people in Rome dressed in designer clothes, tight jeans and wore expensive shoes and sunglasses. I wanted to be Italian and look cool, dress sharply and boldly say 'Pronto' on my mobile phone, wearing designer shades with black, gelled hair. I wanted to drive a retro Fiat 500 with a rasping engine, down an old and shiny wet cobbled street as the tyres made rippling noises.

I felt weak and shivery for most of the day. I had a slight cough which might have been due to feeling cold during the night, and I was sneezing a lot more than usual: maybe as an allergic reaction to the blanket.

We had not eaten breakfast, and it was getting late, so we popped into a local cafe and drank cappuccinos and ate cake. I was not a coffee drinker and preferred builder's tea, but the Italians make exceptional coffee: a creamy texture and a frothy topping served in small cups at the just the right temperature and ready before you have even finished asking for it! Not like in English cafes, where you seem to wait for an eternity while dials and levers are pressed on a machine, similar to a quirky Wallace and Gromit contraption, producing a beverage which never cools down, served in an oversized cup that would be more fitting on the film set of *Alice in Wonderland.*

I left Halise to have a smoke at the cafe, and, ironically, visited a pharmacy to buy cough medicine. On my return to the cafe, she was asking an elderly man for the directions to Piazza di Spagna (at the bottom of the Spanish steps). He explained it well, in his strong accent, and we understood. Shortly after, we boarded a bus to see the famous French designed and built steps. Their sole purpose was for the French to access the Spanish district in Rome. We later walked down some narrow streets lined with more designer shops.

On our way to the Trevi Fountain, we bought take-away pizza and Coke, walking past a camera shop. I told Halise I wanted to see if they could repair my camera, as the shutter would not open, and I tried my best to understand a man who explained, in broken English, that it was faulty. He Sellotaped the shutter open so I could take photographs for the rest of our trip.

At first, the Trevi Fountain was difficult to see, due to the large crowds throwing coins into the small pool. However, I squeezed my way through to take a sneaky photograph. Luckily, the crowds cleared, so we sat down on a small ledge and ate our food, then took more photographs, and continued on towards the Pantheon.

'Now, that's something you don't see every day!' I quipped, as I noticed Roman ruins littering the streets like debris.

We needed to rest, but carried on walking regardless, until we arrived at the Colosseum, positioned next to the Via Sacra (Sacred Road). We sat down and marvelled at the impressive sight before us. The amphitheatre looked phenomenal, although, over time, it had been damaged by various earthquakes, wars and pollution.

We found out from general passers-by that the Pope was due to lead the crucifixion of Christ ceremony that evening, on Good Friday – a poignant moment for everyone watching and a crucial time in the Christian calendar.

We waited until 9 p.m. for the service to start. Squashed against the barriers, we were not going anywhere; but we had secured a good viewing point from which to see the imminent arrival of Pope John Paul II. Halise talked to a tall and handsome guard about the day's events and we remained there for some time. Although we had a glimpse of the Pope, which felt exhilarating, we were shivering as the temperature quickly dropped.

We left and stumbled across a restaurant and ate yet more pizza – our staple diet! I spotted a teacher from our school and shouted his name, running after him down the street! I found him, luckily, and he joined us for a meal. It turned out that Michael had been travelling around Italy alone and we ended up getting drunk in a small bar on the corner of a street, packed full of locals, although Michael left before midnight. By this point, we were both tired and cold, and I was feeling sick from too much cheap red wine. Once we arrived at the hostel, we crashed out on our beds, only to wake up fully dressed the following morning.

Much later that day, we walked to the Vatican Museum, and saw an incredible collection of art in countless rooms and courtyards, including the Sistine Chapel, and stood there completely in awe of Michelangelo's frescos painted on the barrel-vaulted ceiling. His fresco of the *Last Judgement* on the end wall was astonishing and bigger than I imagined; it had taken around four years to paint! I immersed myself in everything before me, and at one point, I forgot about Halise!

I walked back through the Vatican's post office and met Halise at the exit point. We were meant to meet up with Michael (the teacher from our school) but he did not arrive.

I bought two Catholic rosaries as gifts and we left the Vatican, heading off to visit the Basilica di San Pietro (St. Peter's Basilica). I left Halise to wander by herself while I queued for around forty minutes, and finally took the lift to Michelangelo's Dome. Unfortunately, I did not see the so-called relics of 'Christ's Cross', or the Holy Lance, or even the famous statue of Michelangelo's *Pietà* (the Virgin Mary holding Jesus). I climbed more than 300 steps of the spiral staircase banging my head several times into the slanted and uneven walls of the dome. It was a strain to walk up the steps but when I reached the top, the views were worth waiting for: the Vatican, St. Peter's Square and cityscape of Rome – all designed symmetrically.

After standing still for several minutes, I carefully walked back down the awkward steps, taking a lift to the Vatican Grottos. I had been told numerous Popes had been buried here, including St. Peter, encased in a tomb, shielded by bulletproof glass designed by NASA.

I stared at the tomb. There were occasional moments in life when I would feel spiritual and at other times I would think that everything in life was just random chaos. Whether or not turning to God was a selfish act, I did it anyway, and on reflection, it should have been the first and only thing I needed to help me in the past. I hoped that if God exists, he could forgive me for not placing my confidence in Him alone.

I continued to stand there looking at this tomb, deep in thought: if the story was true, then this man baptised Christ – what a responsibility!

I never knew the correct way to pray (if there was a correct way?). Was I supposed to think or speak to God? Should I kneel down or stand up? Should I put my hands together or keep my hands in my pockets? Should I open or close my eyes? Should I look up or look down? Should I look obvious or remain discreet? I knew people were walking past me but I did not see them and I did not really care what they thought.

I stayed where I was and then looked down. I did not know what to ask for but I wanted to pray to God at this moment and I kept thinking and asked God in my mind. 'What should I do?'

I continued to stand there. I needed this moment of solitude and reflection despite all the people around me. Suddenly, I saw a picture in my mind of an old, rusty American car in a big cotton field - of all things! Was that just wishful thinking?

I returned to St. Peter's Square, stumbling across Halise. She had also met Leonardo, but this was no dead artist, this one was alive and kicking and for the first time in a while, Halise had a sparkle in her bright green eyes.

At first, he appeared to be a nice person and proudly drove us around in his Alfa Romeo to Campo de' Fiori (one of the main squares in Rome) where we ate paninis. After telling us he owned a TV company, I quickly became cynical and thought he was just out to impress her – he seemed too relaxed and, strangely, I was wary within

57

minutes of meeting him.

We left him, made our way to the Piazza Venezia (the central hub of Rome) and then walked back to the hostel. Halise went inside and I went to get my hair cut by a barber next door. Despite the only communication being in very simplified and over-animated sign language, I managed to leave the barbers feeling rather pleased with my new 'Italian haircut' – all I needed now was a pair of designer sunglasses!

I popped back to the hostel to tell Halise that I was going to use a computer for a while, and all she wanted to do was relax. I looked up the website that advertised the jobs in America and the main places to work were indeed, Atlanta, Virginia, Utah and North Carolina. Again, North Carolina stood out, not because Utah is a state notoriously full of Mormons, or because I didn't want to dodge bullets in Atlanta or climb mountains in Virginia; North Carolina just seemed to have a certain charm about it.

In the hostel, we met a group of friendly travellers who asked us to go on an Italian pub crawl: Leah (American), Nicholas (German, quiet and good-looking), Hans from Belgium (and annoying) and Vanessa from Australia (who was overly friendly, despite my current rather negative views on Australians!).

We had free shots in each pub, and each one was more lethal than the last. We also had a free drink in one pub and bought drink cards for ten euros each, followed by a random guided tour organised by two other people we met (Chris and Sam); I had never consumed as much alcohol as this before.

I talked to Sam about a city named Charlotte in North Carolina. She told me it has a sub-tropical climate, and has many houses with shutters on their windows. We left the last pub in the early hours and walked around aimlessly, bumping into Leonardo again, who kindly gave us a lift back to the hostel – at least he offered an efficient 'taxi service', despite his peculiar character! We concluded, he was probably, of all things, a drug-dealer! We arrived back at the hostel and fell asleep instantly.

We woke up late the following morning, still feeling tired and drunk, after our busy exploits the day before. Sadly, we missed the Pope's speech in St. Peter's Square and, as it was raining, we decided to use the Metro instead. We walked around the market near the Vatican eating dried fruit and leisurely ambled through the streets of Rome for several hours. I do not know how I managed to do that with a hangover from hell.

We arrived back at the hostel late afternoon and, again, I had the urge to browse the Internet and look at these places in North Carolina, despite feeling groggy.

I was becoming increasingly curious and was slightly more knowledgeable about this state: its capital is Raleigh, contains many cotton and cornfields in rural areas and has some strangely named towns - Boone, Cary, Clayton, Asheville, Apex, Arapahoe, Ahoskie, Fuquay-Varina, Tarboro and Wake Forest, to name just a few. I quite liked these names although they did seem to have something quirky about them and I imagined old men with grey beards, wearing checked shirts, distilling whiskey in front of wooden shacks, just like the peeling Jack Daniel's adverts I had often seen plastered on the walls of the London Underground. The names just sounded typically 'American' and apparently, there are over 500 cities, towns and villages in North Carolina.

I felt 'excited' as we had been invited out for dinner with Leah, Nicholas, Vanessa, Hans, and two Joes also came (one from Ohio and a teacher from London). We caught the Metro, then walked at a leisurely pace for over forty-five minutes to the famous Trastevere district, feeling overwhelmed by the maze of narrow, cobbled streets.

We went to a busy restaurant called Sette Oche (7 Geese), and the food was delicious, although the service was slow.

I suddenly blurted out in my drunken state, 'This is making me realise that life has more to offer than being depressed over some broken relationship', which generated some laughter, smiles and nods of appreciation from my newly befriended small crowd, especially Halise, who winked with affirmation.

As everyone talked around me, I had a flashback as I remembered meeting Nick, one sunny Saturday afternoon at a bar in Central

London. His main intention was to receive his unopened post, yet mine was just to see him. His post had built up into a large pile since the break-up and his departure.

I offered to deliver it to him personally, although in hindsight that was a grave error of judgement, as I stupidly wanted to meet him, even though I knew it would have been painful. The sensible thing to do was to forward it to his work address and avoid all physical contact with him.

My emotions had taken over and my heart was thumping in my chest, and I remember waiting for him in the bar as a drank a bottled beer. When he arrived, I felt anxious yet full of anticipation. Within minutes of his arrival, my mobile rang. 'Just one minute', I said and dealt with the call quickly because I wanted this moment with him to last as long as possible.

'Is that your shag?' Nick exclaimed in response after I ended the call. The comment seemed divisive and strangely comical from his point of view but brutal from mine and I just smiled, trying to brush it off. Nick checked his mobile several times, producing the odd smile as he did so. Maybe he was happier or his new partner knew of our meeting.

After a couple of drinks, an exchange of the post and a somewhat awkward conversation, we parted. I felt numb and saddened inside. I should not have put myself through that experience. This person, with whom I had once been so intimate, now felt like a stranger.

Coolly, he said goodbye and left hurriedly, going in the opposite direction to me. It was a strange feeling. I looked back but Nick kept walking briskly away. Did he really have no feelings left or had he just moved on? That was the last time I ever saw him.

As I sat on the train home and stared through the window, I thought about his comment on my phone call. The caller was a female work colleague asking how I was. I think from that moment, I saw the bigger picture. Despite my feelings, I just had to forget about him and move on.

At the restaurant in Trastevere, I drifted in and out of the conversation but remembered enjoying the discussions about food, wine, people, cities and Rome. I never really had conversations like this with Nick but there was no doubt, I wanted to keep the relationship going – just because I was in love with him.

I wanted to keep in touch with our new friends Hans, Nicholas and Leah (who promised to send us photographs). However, I was tired and asked Halise if we could leave.

We caught a bus back to Termini station, then made our way to the hostel and went straight to bed, exhausted.

We woke around 9 a.m., showered, quickly packed our bags without talking and left an hour later. I looked in my pocket and saw that Sam had given me his email address, which I had forgotten about.

For breakfast, we ate ham and cheese panini and chips, and drank cappuccinos. We arrived in Naples and changed trains, catching one to Sorrento, and then walked to the campsite. We ate at the campsite restaurant and went to bed early.

It was our last day in Italy and I was feeling quite morose. Halise had done nothing wrong to provoke these feelings but maybe, deep down, I was not looking forward to going home. I had enjoyed this holiday too much.

We quickly looked around the shops in Sorrento and Halise bought a pair of jeans. I told her I wanted to see Mount Vesuvius and Pompeii, and she was happy to continue shopping.

I missed the train for Mount Vesuvius and while waiting on the platform, I met a man called Keith with a strong Scouse accent. He was quite old and said he knew a person who lived in Atlanta who taught Tai Chi. He also mentioned that he had met a couple from Detroit and said that Atlanta was a 'great city!'

I was now seriously thinking that teaching in America would be a positive decision; coming to Italy had been a defining step for me and had certainly had an influence on making this decision. I just wanted to turn a negative situation into a positive one and I was, in fact, feeling stronger.

I got off the train at Pompei Scavi and I had just missed the last bus to the volcano, so I walked into a square full of taxis and shared one with an Italian man and Belgian couple.

It took a while to get there and it was a bumpy ride up the rugged road towards Vesuvius. We paid the taxi driver and then it cost a further six euros to enter the volcano site. It took about another thirty minutes or so to walk up the volcano itself. I also rented a walking stick for two euros and then paid another six euros to enter the crater site. This turned out to be an expensive walk!

I took many photographs of the smoking crater within its planetary landscape – towering 1,000 metres above sea level – and admired the panoramic views of Sorrento, Capri and Naples. I suddenly remembered someone once saying to me, 'Italians say you have to see Naples before you die!' Unfortunately, I would not get to see this, so called, 'great city' on this trip.

The taxi driver stopped several times and advised me to take photos of the extinct lava flows. I walked briskly down the volcano, creating a cloud of powered red dust behind me – a liberating feeling. Luckily, further down, the same taxi was waiting, and I paid him an extravagant amount of money for him to drive me to Pompeii and wait for me, but unfortunately it was closed!

I ran to the back of the building and sneakily and quickly entered the museum, as this was my only opportunity. I quickly looked around the Lost City, taking photographs of the three people and animals preserved in ashes from the volcanic eruption that happened in AD79. I had only recently seen photographs of these and read about it in a textbook at school, coincidentally, a few days before we came on the trip when I covered a geography lesson.

I felt cheeky as I took my last photograph of the preserved people, then ran back to the waiting taxi and we sped off towards Sorrento. Still coated in a film of red dust, I met up with Halise, who was in the same shopping centre.

Sorrento was spectacular, but we only had a few hours to see it before we caught the bus back to Rome the following morning. Our flight to London was at 2 p.m., and we slept for most of it.

I was feeling happy and optimistic about my future, and I was looking forward to being back in London so I could apply for this new teaching position in America. I knew this would be a positive yet challenging opportunity but it was the obvious next step, and now felt the perfect time.

Italy had been a country of love, healing and beauty.

I started to swim in that deep, cold ocean, and in the far distance, I could see land.

11

Late April 2003

'Someone looks happy!' the school receptionist confidently stated, as she smiled brightly, across her desk.

As usual, I swiped my identity card across the surface of the metal security machine. 'I take it you had a good Easter then?' she asked.

'Yes! It was great, thanks.' I beamed a big smile back at her. She was right, I did feel very happy. This time last week, I had been in Italy feeling reflective, retrospective and at times, cynical about life, but now I was back in Crystal Palace feeling upbeat and optimistic, although I resisted telling her where I had been.

'How was yours?'

'I just stayed at home, mainly sorting the kids out. The little buggers!' she scoffed.

'I am sure it was nice.' I liked her humour and she always seemed happy greeting everyone with a huge grin each morning – a very good trait.

'It was, actually!' she replied.

'I had better get going, got a lot to do, first day back an' all!'

'I know. Have a good day!' she said quite loudly but in a friendly way, as I walked up the stairs towards the science corridor.

'THANKS. YOU TOO!' I roared back, as I walked away.

It always felt 'peculiar' going back to school, especially after some time off, but having been to another country meant it was even more of a shock to the system and took me a day or two to get back into a normal routine.

It was nice seeing everyone at work – the teachers and the kids – but I struggled through the busy first day and I did not have the chance to speak to many people, including Halise.

Finally, the summer term had arrived and it felt like there was light at the end of the tunnel. The Year 11s would soon start study leave and their lessons now involved revision: material that they had

64

forgotten about or had not listened to during the year.

The days were now longer and warmer as the summer holidays quickly approached. Teachers were busier than ever, preparing students for their imminent GCSEs and everyone was rushing around in a chaotic fashion, but this was the home straights. In just over two months, the school year would be over and with time fast disappearing, I had to make that call to VIF soon. I still had the advert in my wallet and decided to make that first phone call the following day.

After making the initial call, an adviser said I would have to write a short essay – this was the first part of the application process; I had to state the reasons why I wanted to work in another country and what skills and experience I could offer. That very day, during a free lesson, I used a computer in the staff room to start writing the essay. It had to be succinct at about two hundred words long and I wrote it straight from the heart, then posted it after school. I received a reply from VIF several days later, saying they liked my statement. I now had to complete the next stage: an application form, which I did over the next couple of days and posted it promptly.

Several weeks before, working in America had just been an idea but it was quickly turning into a possibility.

I received another letter from VIF inviting me to attend an interview at their London offices, strangely, on a Saturday. I knew there were no guarantees, yet I felt focused and determined. I imagined already that I had the job in America – it was a state of mind.

It had been two weeks since writing that first letter and I was travelling on the train to Victoria station, dressed in a dark grey suit, ready for my interview. I read my scribbled notes several times, looking up once as the train passed the iconic Battersea Power Station. I read the invitation letter one more time, as the train stopped.

The directions on the invitation letter were easy to follow and upon arrival, I looked up at the glass and steel building reflecting the bright sunshine. I walked through the revolving door, walked up to an elderly man wearing a security outfit, complete with a black cap, who sat at a reception desk in the foyer. After stating who I was and why I was there, he slowly moved his index finger down a long list of names, nodded, pointed to the lift and told me to go to the third floor.

'There is a waiting room on the right when you come out of the lift', he said kindly and quietly – his only words.

I arrived in the waiting room, sat down, and looked through my notes again. I was there for several minutes before the door of the interview room opened.

'Mr Wood?'

'Yes.' I looked up at him and smiled.

'Would you like to come in?'

He smiled back and ushered me into the small interview room containing another man and a woman, all standing and waiting to greet me, and in turn we shook hands.

'It is lovely to meet you!' one of them said. He was about five-foot ten and smartly dressed in a dark suit. He also wore glasses with heavy frames and had a friendly face. He was well spoken and gracefully gestured with his hand to a chair on the opposite side of the desk. Once we had all sat down, the woman introduced herself. She was dressed in a dark business suit, quite small in height with a plump figure. The interview began.

'Hello! Ahhm Vicki and ahh am the pl-ay-cement officer for Vee-Ah-Ey-f.' She smiled again. Her accent was friendly, slow and every word pronounced and drawn out. I started smiling anxiously at first, but this quickly became a big 'Cheshire Cat' grin.

Vicki looked straight at me. 'Is every th-y-ing okay?'

I paused before answering. 'I don't want to sound out of turn, but your American accent just makes this situation seem very real.'

They all giggled discreetly, looking at each other, following what I instantly considered a foolish remark. I was not sure if I broke the ice or embarrassed her or myself. Maybe I sounded utterly ridiculous or inappropriate.

'Well, Pauuul ... thank yew. This is definitely real!' She started laughing and I still felt embarrassed by what I had just said.

She continued, 'I feel quite self-conscious now!' and she giggled again. 'Pauuul, ahh would just firstly like to introduce Pe-d-er, he is the recruitment consultant, and Andrew who is the administra-der, and

66

he will be dealing with all of yer documentation.' Peter and Andrew smiled and nodded.

I had just thirty minutes to prove to them (and myself) that this is what I really wanted. I had to concentrate on what she was saying and not how she was saying it.

I smiled back at all of them and thought the next twenty minutes or so could change my life.

After several minutes, the interview was in full flow.

Each person on the panel asked questions, some of which related to my statement, and mostly these developed into short discussions. We talked a lot and all I remember were the questions: 'What can you offer to the programme? How can you be an ambassador of your country' and 'What skills would you employ in the USA?'

I tried to answer each question in the best way I could. I said, 'Educating American students is important, not just because of my subject, but because of my culture and country – I would like to expand their minds culturally, as well as academically.'

They seemed to like my answers and nodded while making notes, looking up and smiling at me, and sometimes at each other, although, I was not sure how convinced they were.

We talked for some time about my present job and about my recent teaching experience, and what my intentions would be if I were a successful candidate. They also asked me about a lesson that had inspired my students. I thought back to the first school I taught at: an inner-city school in a deprived area of London, where I taught a small class of students from underprivileged backgrounds who had Special Educational Needs. I showed them an experiment using old chipped glass prisms, trying to separate white light into its seven colours, which, thankfully, worked. Miraculously, it started raining on a sunny day towards the end of the lesson, producing the clearest rainbow in the sky, linking the lesson nicely to an actual real-life event. I will never forget the look on their innocent and surprised faces, even though they had troubles in their lives – it was humbling and rewarding.

The interview seemed to go well and progress quickly. Some parts of the interview seemed informal, relieving some of the pressure. I remembered some of the notes I had prepared and during the last few minutes of the interview, I focused on my experiences as a teacher. As the interview concluded, Vicki spoke: 'Well, that's all the questions that we need to ask, Pauuul. Do yew have any questions that yew want to ask us?'

I had previously thought of some questions to ask but at this point, my mind went blank for a few seconds, briefly creating an awkwardness, and strangely, I suddenly felt nervous.

'… could I please ask what the next stage of the interview process is?'

'Well, yew have completed all three stages: the essay, the application form and now the interview, and I must say, it's all looking pre-ddy good, so don't worry! Once we have reviewed all of your information, we w-yill let yew know. We w-yill send yew a le-dder, which yew should receive in the next few days, informing yew of the outcome.'

'If you were offered a position to work on our programme, would you accept?' Andrew asked.

I looked over at all three of them, paused and smiled, before saying: 'Definitely.' I had read an article that you should always maintain eye contact throughout an interview and I did just that, and instinctively, this felt right.

They all smiled and stood up, as Andrew politely opened the door for me to leave the room. 'W-yell, we w-yill no-dif-aa yew in the next few days, and this w-yill give yew adequate taame to accept or, if yew so wish, declaane the offer.' Vicki smiled again.

As I smiled back, I shook their hands in turn, and told them all it was 'a pleasure meeting you.' As I arrived in the reception area, the same man nodded silently as I left the building and caught a train back home.

Three days later, a letter from VIF arrived.

17 May 2003

Dear Mr Wood,

The Visiting International Faculty enjoyed meeting you.

We are delighted to offer you a teaching position and we would like
to congratulate you as a VIF Cultural Exchange Ambassador. You will
be working in the State of North Carolina, as this was the first area of
your choice. You will fly out on the 17th July 2003. Further details
regarding the orientation days, contracts, schedules and the flights will
arrive in the post shortly.

Again, we would like to offer our congratulations on choosing to
work for our Programme. Please read, sign, and return the enclosed
letter of acceptance in the envelope provided. We hope that you will
be very happy working for VIF.

Please do not hesitate to contact us if you have any further
questions.

Our orientation team look forward to meeting you once you arrive
in North Carolina.

Yours sincerely,

VIF Programme

12

Within days of receiving the confirmation letter from VIF, I resigned from my job, giving a notice period of six weeks – quite a short amount of time considering I had served four long years at that school. I had to finish my period of notice earlier, as my scheduled flight to America was 3 days before the end of term. The only major school events I would miss would be the final whole school assembly (when kids jeered at teachers who were leaving), a free outdoor buffet (with copious amounts of free wine provided) and the leaving speeches. However, I was kindly granted permission to leave the school on Friday, 11 July.

The last days of school only involved holding quizzes, doing experiments that I never had the time to do in the year or showing films, to the delight of the students. The internal and public examination period was now over and the teachers and students had wound down a little, as they were all tired. Just like everyone else, I too longed for the summer holidays, although this time round, my holiday would be rather eventful.

My last day at the school arrived and my department bought me a nice leather-bound notebook, as a leaving present, which I could use as a journal. They were a great bunch, and I would miss them, including Halise, the staff, the kids and the school.

Over the last six weeks, I had been busily organising my flat most evenings and weekends in preparation for renting it out through a letting agent. I had spent time carefully and methodically packing my belongings and personal items into several cardboard boxes, with the intention of leaving my flat fully furnished while I was working in America.

The letting agency found a nice young couple to move in on the weekend I was moving out. They gave me the opportunity to meet them to exchange mobile numbers and email addresses to give me

70

peace of mind (even though I was paying the agency a small fee). My new tenants also had copies of the keys and a tenancy agreement.

I had recently sold my car to a friend, who had collected it the day before I left London and this extra cash came in useful for my imminent departure. Everything was organised for my big move: the flat, the car, the packing and now, it was just a matter of days before my flight to America.

I hired a small van to transport all my personal belongings back to Rochdale. My brother and sister- in-law had kindly driven the van down the previous night and stayed over at my flat, which contained a mountain of boxes in the bedroom. After making them a cooked breakfast the following morning, they helped me load everything into the van, including Jack in his cat carrier, and by lunchtime on Saturday, 12 July, we were ready to leave.

As we walked towards the van, my brother seemed eager to start the drive back to Rochdale – driving was something he had always enjoyed. Before we reached the van, I suddenly said, 'Do you mind if I go back inside the flat one more time, just to check everything is okay?'

'Yeah, course you can! We don't know the way home anyway!' my sister-in-law said quickly, speaking with her warm, regional accent in a very jovial manner.

Back in the flat, I looked around one last time, walking into each room. I was not thinking about anything in particular but I just needed a few minutes on my own, to collect my thoughts and give me time to reflect. As I did this, I perched myself on the edge of the sofa. Everything was tidy and clean, the carpets were hoovered and the furniture highly polished – the flat was spotless (thanks to my sister-in-law who made sure everything looked perfect, ready for my new tenants).

I stood up and then walked slowly around every room, feeling melancholy; finally, I walked back into the kitchen where my shoes clicked on the freshly cleaned, laminated flooring. I had always loved this small flat – I had some happy memories (and sad ones) – but I was ready to leave it behind, for a while.

I walked over to the large kitchen window, prised the steel venetian

71

blinds open and looked outside at the bright sunshine. Pulling my fingers out of the two cold strips of metal, I looked around at the minimal modern-looking kitchen: white walls, wooden units, laminate flooring, stainless-steel cooker and a steel extractor fan. Again, everything looked shiny, clinical and perfectly organised.

'Am I doing the right thing?' I quietly asked.

As I looked around from the window, back at the full view of the kitchen one last time, I saw something in my peripheral vision. I looked back again, noticing a distorted white shape which looked like a small bright cross, just two or three inches high, on the wall opposite the kitchen window underneath the cupboards. I looked back at the blind and again at the wall two or three times with increasing curiosity, thinking I was seeing things. This was either an illusion or just beams of light from the bright sunshine coming through the blind and reflecting off the white wall. Normally, I would have analysed such a situation with a scientific perspective, but on this particular occasion, I did not know what to think.

I walked slowly down the cream carpeted staircase, stopping on the bottom step, trying to make sense of what I had just seen and felt. I had a flashback to my time in Rome, the moment I prayed. Maybe, this was another answer. Just before I opened the door and left the flat for the last time, I looked back up the staircase and smiled, feeling calmed by what I had seen. Whatever it was, whatever it meant, I left the flat feeling peaceful and reassured that everything would be okay and I kept it to myself.

It was quite a stressful drive through the busy London traffic, and we pulled over at a petrol station on the A4 to have a quick bite to eat at a neighbouring cafe. Then I swapped seats with my brother and he drove the rest of way on the motorways, and we arrived back in Rochdale several hours later.

Our dad was there to greet us and after a cup of tea and a chat about the drive and the last couple of days, we unloaded the van and placed boxes, pictures and bin liners full of clothing on the large front lawn. I later thanked my brother and sister-in-law for all of their help and, once they had left, I spent the rest of the day packing everything away.

I gave Jack to my dad to look after, which he did not mind. In fact, I think my Dad welcomed some new company but I knew Jack would feel unsettled for a while, and I would miss him. There were big changes about to happen for everyone, including Jack, and at that point, I had not realised how significant these changes would be.

After an exhausting day, I had a TV dinner with my dad. The atmosphere between us was sombre as I knew, deep down, he was not too happy about me going to work in America. Maybe I was being selfish, making this decision, but I knew it would not be forever.

We watched TV but didn't talk much; the day's events and the build-up over the last few weeks had caught up with me and, after snoozing on the sofa several times, I went to bed early. I still wanted to check my luggage and make sure I had the all the correct documentation, ready for the flight. As I lay in bed, thoughts of my recent efforts at organisation and preparation raced through my mind: seeing the advert, applying for the job in America, the interview, resigning from my school, renting out my flat, the letting agency, transporting all my belongings here, rearranging my finances and getting to this point of making sure everything was in place. Exhausted, I soon fell asleep.

I needed time to relax and enjoy being with my dad, so I spent all my time with him over the next few days, and it was a relief to not have the responsibility of running my own home, if only temporarily. Staying with him brought back lots of childhood memories and made me think about my dad's kindness and popularity. I liked the idea of being a 'child' again and I warmed to the feeling of living at home – I think my dad did too.

I woke up early on Thursday, 17 July, feeling excited, yet anxious. My dad had kindly planned to take the day off work in order to come with me to Manchester Airport; however, as he did not drive, my aunt offered to take us all there. The flight was not until 2.30 p.m., although I had to check in two hours before.

During breakfast, I talked and laughed with my dad and played with Jack. After we had finished eating, I went upstairs to check my luggage. I had one large suitcase and a holdall, which contained a transparent plastic wallet holding my passport, I-94 visa (which I had collected from the American Embassy a few days earlier) and other important letters from VIF regarding my orientation days on my arrival.

My aunt arrived. I placed my luggage in the hallway near the front door and as we were about to leave, Jack slowly walked over to me and looked up at me. I picked him up and kissed him – I think he knew I was leaving.

We loaded the car and set off. There was light conversation for most of the journey, although my dad was quite perky. The motorway was busy, slightly delaying our journey, but we arrived in plenty of time. After parking the car, we all walked into the departure lounge at Manchester Airport.

'Your flight number is on the board', my aunt observantly pointed out. She had always been astute, despite being unsteady on her feet and having a multitude of health problems. Her mind was alert and enquiring, although at times, she came across as quite abrupt, but it was just her manner.

'You are flying with American Airlines!' she stated. My dad did not say anything.

'Yeah, it's a nine-hour flight to Atlanta, where I get my connecting flight to North Carolina.'

My dad spoke quietly and suddenly: 'What time will you arrive?' His eyes looked sad and watery. I knew he would get emotional.

'I think around eleven tonight. Don't worry dad, I will be okay. I promise I will call you as soon as I can.' I am not sure if my reassurances worked. I checked in, showed my passport and travel documents to the airport authorities, sparking up a short conversation with a polite woman at the check-in desk.

'You need to go to gate thirty-one, as the flight will be boarding quite soon', she explained. 'Have a good flight', she smiled at me.

'Thank you', I replied, smiling back.

As I turned around, my dad and aunt were standing there talking to each other. Maybe my reassuring words had eased the mood after all, but I still worried about him.

It was time. I hugged my dad: a strange feeling, the first time really, since being a child. 'Dad, I will give you a ring once I have arrived. Don't worry.'

I hugged and kissed my aunt and put my arms around my dad one more time. We had never really shown affection as a family in this way. I think it was more of a generational thing but I do not remember hugging when I was young; but it was a good feeling and I wished we had done it more.

I started to walk away, looking back and waving goodbye, which they did in response. I looked around one more time and waved, which made me feel sad, even though I braved a smile. I felt guilty leaving my dad behind, but he knew that I had to do this – he never tried to stop me, just quietly supported me.

From a distance, I lip-read his final words: 'Look after yourself.'

13

Hartsfield-Jackson Atlanta International Airport looked as big as a city – and I wanted to live there.

People walked chaotically and randomly in all directions, rushing for their flights not just within the USA but all over the world. I could not believe the number of gates it had: over 200! Apparently, it is the world's busiest airport, with over 200,000 people passing through it every day. Looking around, it really felt the entire world's population was in there; I just stood there in awe of its sheer size, as a river of people streamed past.

I slept during most of the flight (except at meal times) and as I waited for my suitcase to move along the ten-mile long conveyer belt, I felt surprisingly energised. I would normally feel wiped out and miserable after any flight, even short hauls, and would just want to crawl into bed at a random hotel; but this time, I was ready to take on the world – maybe it was the anticipation of my new American adventure.

The flight had arrived late and by the time I had got off the plane, collected my luggage (although I was surprised to find it!) and walked half-mesmerised back inside the airport, stopping several times to marvel its size, I had missed my connecting flight to North Carolina by just two minutes.

'OH GOD, NOOOO!' I cried out, staring hopelessly as my jaw dropped while I watched what should have been my plane taking off into the night sky.

A passing man stopped in his tracks. 'Is everythin' okay?'

'Not really ... I missed my ... flight! SHIT!'

'Just get the next one!' he casually remarked.

'What do you mean?' I turned to look at him with a confused and irritated expression. He remained calm, but I was about to go into nuclear meltdown.

'You're Bri-dish right?' he asked inquisitively.

I felt defensive even though I thought it sounded obvious. I just opened and closed my mouth but no words came out. I was still in shock.

'Yeah; look at that board there, it shows all the domestic flights in the US.' I carried on looking at him and stared at his finger pointing for several seconds as he indicated towards the board. 'There!' he said more loudly, jabbing his finger forwards.

I slowly moved my head along an invisible line from his pointing, index finger to the super-sized departure board – literally right in front of my face.

'Ah!' He must have thought I was some kind of half-wit and he started laughing.

'Hey don't worry. This happens to people all the time, especially if you don't know how things work here. I love the Bri-dish accent. Just gets me, every time', he said excitedly.

I raised a smile, nodded and felt more relaxed and less conscious that I had just made a complete fool of myself; I closed my jaw, finally getting over the shock of missing my flight. I quite liked the instant recognition of being British.

'Sorry, I've never missed a flight before and I just panicked. Call me stupid, but flights within America are called domestic flights, right?' (I was already starting to use some Americanisms.)

'Yes Sir! All flights to and from other countries are international flights. Hey, you'll pick it up soon enough!'

'Sorry, by the way, I am Paul. I've just arrived here.' I put my hand out ready to shake his.

'Hi Pauuul. I'm Mark. Pleased to meet you.'

He had the biggest grin on his face and shook my hand with a firm grip, keeping eye contact with me all the time. Mark was about my height, had a stockier build, was blonde and wore glasses. He dressed smartly and carried a small brown case. At a rough guess, he must have been in his mid-fifties. He seemed warm, friendly and interested in talking.

'Is this your first time in the States?' he asked.

'Yes, I mean no, I have been here twice before. New York and Boston, but that was several years ago, before, I mean.' He looked bewildered, as what I said made little sense.

'Hey, are you okay?' he asked genuinely.

'Yeah … yeah, I'm fine. I'm just a bit tired, probably, and a bit, overwhelmed, I guess.'

'Right. How long are you gonna be in the US for?'

'Oh, I don't know how long yet, it depends on my new job.' Despite his growing interest in my life, I felt irritated because I was worried about missing another flight.

'So, you are going to be living here too? That seemed a rather obvious question, sorry! Wow, it's all new for you! Have only been to the States before to visit?'

'Yes. I have been before, on holiday, I mean … vacation.' Correcting myself instantly, it was now beginning to feel like the Spanish inquisition.

'It's okay, I know what you mean. We sometimes say holidays here too! Get used to it, you will have to do a lotta of translating when you get to North Carolina, believe me! I take it that's where you headin'?' As he glanced at the departure board.

'Really?' I looked at him concerned.

'Oh, yeah', he affirmed. 'What's your line of work, Pauuul?' (I liked the way he pronounced my name.)

'I will be a teacher in North Carolina.' My answers were now more factual and shorter.

'You will definitely need a translator then!' he continued giggling to himself.

'I'm actually worried now.' I secretly looked at the departure board and then back at him and grinned.

'I'm sure you'll be fine. They will love you, and they will love your accent even more. It is a beau-diful state. You will love it. Look, I had be-dder catch my flight, Pauuul. I wish you the best of luck with your new venture!'

He started to walk away but then stopped again and turned around. 'Oh yeah. Pauuul. The "oh God" thing.'

'Sorry?'

'You're in the deep South now. You might wanna keep a track on what you're sayin!'

'Oh yeah! I didn't think about that.'

'I was just kiddin ya, man, but this is the Bible Belt, remember?' He winked and smiled.

'I hope I didn't offend you Mark?'

'Not ad - all!'

He shook my hand firmly again and started to walk away backwards. 'Bye and thanks for your help.'

'No problem! I wish you well. Stay calm; there will be another flight to North Carolina soon. Enjoy America!'

'Thank you. Bye!' I smiled and looked back at him. He was a nice guy. 'It was good to meet you, Pauuul.'

I watched him walk away. I felt befriended yet regrettably irritated, only because I had missed my flight. Within seconds, he disappeared, merging into a vast crowd of people. I was grateful he had taken time to help me.

He had calmed my nerves in a short space of time, made me feel welcome in a strange airport, in a strange country and had quickly explained some golden rules that I was sure would come in useful.

I smiled and looked back at the departure board. My next flight to Raleigh-Durham was, in fact, in eighteen minutes. How cool. It was similar to missing a train: if you miss a flight, you just catch the next one. That simple! I never thought flights in America would be that regular. Moments later, there was an announcement.

'The next flight to Raleigh-Durham is now boarding. Make your way to gate fifty-nine.'

I boarded the small chartered passenger jet, which had two rows of grey leather seats, and I noticed the dimly glowing blue lights in the cabin and that there appeared to be only a few other passengers spaced around the cabin.

Within minutes, the engines roared loudly and with a high-pitched sound we were propelled to a high speed and took off. I felt very conscious I was flying as the plane banked left, shortly after take-off.

The grey leather seats felt cold and smelt new on this almost empty flight and shortly after take-off we were served small packets of

79

peanuts and chilled orange juice. I felt like some kind of VIP! I was quite excited and spent most of the night flight staring out of a small window transfixed by the hazy lights on the ground far below. The lights started to look brighter as we neared the airport. The flight seemed to be over before it had begun. There was another announcement:

'We will soon be landing at Raleigh-Durham airport. Please make sure you have fastened your safety belts. We hoped you enjoyed your flight and we look forward to you flying with Delta Airlines in the near future.' The female voice spoke in dulcet tones in a mild American accent, making me feel I was sinking into a bed of giant marshmallows. I looked around the plane again and thought, I could really get used to this.

Once we had arrived at Raleigh-Durham Airport (RDU), which was tiny in comparison to the one in Atlanta, it did not take long before I was collecting my suitcase and leaving the airport.

It was dark and muggy outside as I walked along a paved area, wheeling my suitcase behind me while holding my hand luggage. I suddenly saw a group of people, huddled together, at what looked like a bus stop, near the airport's entrance. There was a white sign above them with the words 'VIF' written in large writing. I walked towards them.

'Hello! I work for VIF, I'm Paul Wood!' I heard giggles in the darkness.

'We thought you were. Yew are the laa-y-st person to arr-aave!'

'Sorry, my flight from England arrived late.'

The inane giggling continued. 'It's okay, these things happen.'

The group of people were all white American hefty-looking females in their twenties who spoke in southern drawl. They were wearing hoodies and tracksuit bottoms covering their oversized bodies, making me feel frail in comparison. One girl hastily grabbed my bag and another lifted my heavy suitcase with ease, placing both into the back of the minibus.

I shrugged my shoulders, took a seat and we drove for forty minutes, arriving at the hotel where I would be staying for the next three days.

14

We parked on the wide drive of the Marriott hotel in downtown Durham, a luxurious and colossal building. At reception, a VIF representative checked me in, and handed over a key and a heavy envelope.

'Hey, yew need to look at the information before yew go to sleep. This is the itinerary for the next three days. Yew c-yan h-yave a laa in tomorrow, so that is naace.' She smiled. 'We wi-y-ll see yew tomorrow', she cheerfully clarified in her southern drawl.

'Thank you.'

In the hotel room, I put my luggage down and quickly opened the letter and read that the first orientation day did not start until 10.30 a.m. the next day. I called my dad, remembering the UK was five hours ahead, and, luckily, he was home and I was happy to hear his voice. Following a reassuring, brief phone call and after a long day of travel, I showered and quickly fell asleep.

I woke surprisingly early the following day, got ready, looked at the schedule again and left the room holding the envelope.

The breakfast area was already busy with people, and as I started to look at the choices, I heard English accents around me. After collecting a hearty fried breakfast and tea on my tray, I stopped and looked at a half empty table.

'Hello, is it okay to sit here?' They all looked up as they ate their food. 'Yeah, sure', and on first impression, they seemed friendly.

It felt strange being single but I knew I was going to meet lots of new people. One of them asked, 'Are you from England?'

'Yeah.'

'We are too', she perkily answered and smiled. I think she was trying to make me feel welcome.

'Cool. I am Paul, nice to meet you all.' It felt reassuring to be around fellow Brits in a similar situation. They all busily devoured their generous portions.

There were two British couples in their twenties: Allison and

Andy, and Rachel and Steve. I immediately thought it must be nice to share an adventure like this with a partner, but as we quickly introduced ourselves, I deliberately put the thought of being on my own to the back of my mind.

'This breakfast is huge! I think I've gained half my body weight, already', Andy confirmed, as he patted his slim waistline and then tucked into another sausage. Everyone looked at him and started laughing as he rubbed his stomach while his mouth was packed full of food – he looked just like a hamster.

Andy seemed a touch cynical and had a dry sense of humour (I did wonder how this would go down with the Americans – maybe they would like it?). He seemed intelligent and witty, but had an interesting charm about him and as the conversation progressed, I noticed he was like a walking-talking encyclopaedia, bombarding us with facts. He also explained everything methodically, but made it interesting and easy to understand. I quite liked him and could relate to his outlook on life. He seemed knowledgeable about America.

'I think we should all weigh ourselves in, this time next year', Alison added.

We all sniggered as we left the table littered with empty plates, cups, saucers, glasses, cutlery and piles of napkins and waddled towards a massive convention room containing hundreds of people.

'This is a bit scary! Shall we all sit together?' Andrew pointed out. I appreciated that they all made me feel welcome, despite being on my own.

There was not much space left in the room but we managed to find a table, with just two people already seated there, situated about two-thirds from the front. We had to squeeze past people as they stood up to let us through, apologising for inconveniencing them.

When we eventually arrived at the table, there was a blonde man, also in his twenties, casually dressed in jeans and white T-shirt, and an older woman wearing a floral dress, around sixty, sitting there together. They seemed deep in conversation and the tall blonde man chuckled randomly, when the older woman was talking to him, and each time he did so, his cheeks turned bright red emphasising his Nordic looks.

After a long and welcoming speech by the director of VIF, we spent the rest of the morning going through formalities. The first talk was about driving: it was explained, in some parts of the state, you could drive at 70 mph on rural interstate highways, but if you were stopped by the police for speeding, it could be considered a serious offence. Once we had been assigned a district to work in, we would be leased a car – something I was looking forward to.

The programme took care of most things: the visa, the car, advice on accommodation, certification in order to teach, finding a suitable school placement and of course, they paid us in US dollars. The salary worked out at $29,000 per year, which seemed a lot, but when converted to pounds and pence, it worked out around £17,000 per year. However, the cost of living was less than in the UK.

We stopped for a coffee break mid-morning. The Brits that I had befriended all went to collect refreshments. English tea was a pleasant surprise and we had cakes too. Standing near the refreshments bar was the blonde man who was sitting at our table earlier. He smiled and introduced himself.

'Hiya, I am Adrian, people just call me Ade.' He then he shook my hand as he burst into a fit of giggles. He reminded me of six-foot four, well-built school child and his casual dress sense was exaggerated by his height. He told us all he used to be in the Marines and then became a history teacher. He had a boyish sense of humour and seemed to laugh at everything. He told us he was from Cheshire. His hair was almost white and nearly matched his T-shirt, and was styled like one of the Gallagher brothers (from the 1990s English rock band, Oasis).

'So, why are you here Ade?' I quietly asked, looking up at him.

Before answering, he casually looked around the large room and then quietly chuckled. 'To meet as many women as possible.'

'C'mon. Seriously?' I asked him again.

'I am being serious. To meet women.'

I looked around the hall and noticed that the majority of the people in the convention room were, indeed, single females.

'Well, looks like you came to the right place then: a meat market before your very own eyes. Is that what you told VIF at the interview?'

I liked his sense of humour and related to him not because he was from the North of England but because he was single.

'What do you think of all the people here then?' I asked.

'They all seem a bit weird, don't you think?'

I laughed as he giggled again. Bizarrely, within minutes of talking, we clicked and chatted away as if we had known each other for longer.

'To be honest, I have not met anyone else here, just you Viffers.'

'Viffers?'

'Yeah!'

'Ha, I like your way of thinking. That's a new code then', I replied.

He giggled again as he gulped down his remaining orange juice and people started walking back into the convention hall.

'I think it's time to go back with all the Viffers!' Ade said.

We slowly walked back while he told me he wanted a break from England and how much he liked America.

Over the next three days, we went through the entire orientation, covering a whole range of activities, including group work; it was quite a rigorous programme, finishing at around 5 pm each day.

We covered the background to VIF (the sponsorship for VIF cultural exchange teachers and their families) and were given a lot of information about the financial and logistical assistance for moving abroad, including travel arrangements and help securing housing and transportation. The next day, we covered US teaching policies, lesson planning, classroom management and cultural adjustments, and how teaching there differed to the UK.

Some experienced VIF teachers talked, explaining their personal stories and how to become a cultural ambassador – some of them even sang! Personally, I was looking forward to talking to the American kids about British culture.

We were also told about the visa system and that you could work for one or two years, tax free or stay for three years and pay tax. You didn't have to make decisions until later and many stayed for three years.

A network of veteran VIF teachers served as local advisers to new teachers. There would be structured, professional development supporting global competence and continuous access to ready-to-use global classroom resources if we needed them, although most schools had their own resources.

At certain points there was information overload (and sometimes my mind wandered and I would start thinking about my new American life). There were also opportunities to contact VIF staff to discuss problems at any time, to learn and share practical tips about cross-cultural communications and there would be regular check-ins with VIF staff and 24/7 emergency support, if needed. The programme seemed tailored to the individual but overall, it was impressive and highly organised.

I had made friends with five people from England (Andy, Allison, Steve, Rachel and Adrian) in the short time I had been there. We had not been outside of this hotel yet but, from what I could gather it was humid and I was trying to get used to converting the temperature into Fahrenheit. I seemed to get on better with Adrian, mainly because he was single like me, although everyone was friendly.

On the last day of orientation, we were called to a room to meet a placement officer and were told we would be working in Johnston County. I did not know much about it, we were just told that the county seat was Smithfield. The main areas were: Smithfield (good for parks, shopping, history, bistros and fishing), Zebulon (which sounded like the name of a distant planet on an episode of *Dr Who* but was famous for parks and hiking), Selma (I kept calling it Semolina, and it also had some parks), Clayton (which had parks, golf and tennis courses) and Benson (which had museums). There were lots of parks in North Carolina and not much else it seemed. Other nearby places included Four Oaks, Kenly, Princeton and Pine Level – all sounding interesting.

We loaded up the minibus and we were all shipped off to a small motel in Smithfield (we had gone down in the world!). There was some food served in the motel and I was sharing a room with Adrian. We spent the whole day in the room just talking and getting to know each other better.

The following day we were driven to a hall in Smithfield to

complete more paperwork and then the exciting part, collecting our leased cars.

We all hurried outside into the warm humid air and went over to a small car park where six different coloured Mitsubishi Mirages were all parked parallel to each other. They looked quite 'used' but I hoped mine would be the British Racing Green one, and to my delight, it was. How ironic!

After one year, you could upgrade to a Mitsubishi Gallant at an increased leasing cost. This was it, we were left to our own devices and we hit the road! I loved driving abroad. All the cars were autos (manuals or gearshifts as they are called there, are rare) and now, we had independence.

I drove excitedly, yet cautiously, back to the hotel, surviving my first short road trip on the interstate. It felt strange, driving at sixty on the big open roads – it seemed effortless driving at a constant speed. The roads were smoother and I did not notice any speed cameras or road works. The next day, we would all find out more about our accommodation and possibly the schools we could be working at.

Five days later, Adrian and I were still in the motel, delirious with boredom and feeling sorry for ourselves. We had no school or accommodation and everybody else had now started his or her American dream – ours felt like the beginning of an American nightmare!

I stared blankly at the TV, as Adrian quietly said, 'Do you know, the Ku Klux Klan was once in this area?' He surreptitiously sipped his bottled beer, looking slightly downtrodden as I turned towards him.

'Are you being serious?' I replied inquisitively and seriously.

'Yes!'

'Shit!'

'What?'

'I want to tell you something.'

'What?'

'I am … gay.'

'I had an idea but it felt rude to ask.'

'I should have told you earlier.'

87

'Hey, it's cool. You didn't have to tell me at all. You are gay, so fucking what!'

Despite telling Ade about my sexuality, and the way he calmly accepted it, I felt shocked about being in an area where the KKK once operated.

'I'm worried now!'

'Why?'

'I just hope I don't get any trouble from people around here.'

'I'm sure you will be ok, these are modern times.'

'I hope so, I had enough of that when I was a kid, so I don't want it now I'm an adult!'

'I'll teach you some moves, don't worry.'

'At least you can look after yourself. You're an ex-Marine for fuck's sake!'

We suddenly laughed like helpless, immature schoolchildren, feeling clueless as to what to expect the following day, and drank more bottles of beer. We became tipsy but it helped us to relax, and deep down, we both hoped that tomorrow would bring better news. In a short space of time, I had become fond of Adrian, warmed to his humour and enjoyed his fellowship. It was like having a mate and a surrogate big brother, despite him being a lot younger.

'It doesn't bother you, me being gay?'

'Will you shut up?' He smiled. 'As long as you don't pounce on me, in the middle of the night', he chuckled and winked.

'Is that what you really think, Mr Irresistible! You better not drink too much then.' I laughed. 'I have heard about you sailors!'

He turned bright crimson, and between his bouts of laughter he said, 'I am what I am and you are what you are. That is the end of this conversation, okay!'

'Affirmative, sailor boy!' I saluted him.

He lifted his bottle towards me, winked and smiled as I clunked my bottle of beer slowly against his, and smiled back.

15

July 2003

I was on the verge of a nervous breakdown; I had no job and I was stuck in an average motel in the middle of an unfamiliar small town, in an unfamiliar country.

However, my situation improved the following morning – I received a call asking me to attend an interview at a middle school in North Johnston County the same afternoon.

I arrived at the school early and waited in the vice principal's office when, suddenly, Allison came out of the adjoining principal's room.

'Hiya!' I said, surprised. 'I didn't know you had an interview here, too?' 'Yeah. I literally found out just this morning!'

'Me too! Did it go okay then?' I asked inquisitively.

She answered with a 'thumbs up' and presented me with a cheeky grin. 'That's great news.'

'It's informal, so don't worry. You'll be fine.'

'It would be good to work in the same school.' As we smiled, the principal came out of his office.

'Good luck', Allison whispered, as she quickly walked away.

The principal looked at me, smiled and greeted me with a firm handshake as he approached.

His name was Raymond Smith, who was probably three times the size of my dad, and my first impression was that he looked a bit fierce; but after quickly introducing himself, and speaking to me quietly with a deep, strong North Carolinian accent, he turned out to be a gentle giant. I could not imagine him being flustered about anything, even during stressful times. Ironically, he shared the same name as my dad.

He invited me to sit opposite him at his desk. He seemed matter of fact, starting the interview immediately.

'How yew doin?' he drawled without looking up.

'I'm fine thanks.'

'Vee-aah-eyf spoke haaly of yew, and we are pleased to meet yew Mr Woo-ood. We do haave a vacancy here, teaching scaa-ence and ma-y-th to eighth graders and if yew des-aade that th-y-is is the place for yew, th-y-en, yew we-yill be teaching scaa-ence and ma-y-th.'

I stared at him for several seconds before answering. 'What does that mean, exactly?'

'Aah a-y-m speaking in in-glish.'

I laughed nervously and avoided further eye contact for several seconds. 'No, I meant, the way you are explaining it, I am a bit … confused?'

Maybe we both needed translators – British to North Carolinian and vice versa. What I really wanted to say was, 'I do not understand a single bloody word you are saying.'

Regardless, he carried on. 'Th-y-at means, yew have one cla-y-as yew w-i-y-ll teach ma-y-th to, and one cla-y-as you will teach scaa-ence and ma-y-th to, and it will be same taam-table, ev-er-y day. B-ya-sically, yew w-i-y-ll see th-y-at cla-y-as yew are teachin' twaace, a whole lot more.' He giggled quietly as I looked back at him strangely.

Despite him speaking slowly, and as I struggled to decipher his words, I was not sure if his laughter was supposed to encourage me to accept the job. I gave him a blank look as he continued to talk.

'Most of these ki-y-ds are from farming backgrounds, and are naace. Yew are gon-na g-y-et the odd one or two th-y-at fools around.'

He paused between every drawn-out word, and as he continued to explain, I tried my hardest to translate every word he said at what seemed the strongest southern accent I had heard so far. It sounded like every word he spoke had exaggerated drawn-out vowel sounds and extra syllables.

'Well, that sounds great', I replied confidently but I didn't really know what else to say.

'Aah know yew taught scaa-ence ba-y-ck in ing-land. Aah c-ay-n see th-a-y-et on yer résumé. Would yew be okay with teachin' ma-y-eth?'

I paused again before answering. 'I have taught maths before but it has been some time.'

'Aam sure yew w-y-ill p-i-yck it ep and yew w-y-ill be workin' closely with Miss P-yen-rose. She will talk yew through everythin'.'

'Thank you. What are the students like?'

'They are of average abilidy, yew g-e-yt some braaght ones, like aah said before, many come from farmin' ba-y-kgrounds. Aah will not laa. Most of the k-i-yds are faane, just the odd one or two th-a-yt can put yer ba-y-ck ep, but don't worry, that's waa we are here.'

I took every word he said (and that I could understand) for gospel. I just could not imagine this man ever being deceitful 'ab-ee-out anyth-y-in'. He seemed open, honest and genuine but teaching maths? - I did wonder.

'Okay, Mr Woo-ood, you're haa-r-ed.' I looked at him in astonishment but quickly worked out he had said 'hired.'

It was as quick and as simple as that! The principal told me I would start working there in August as the school year started much earlier in the US compared to the UK (then again, they break up earlier, too).

'Well, Mr Woo-ood. Aah would laake to offer yew the position, if yew-ar appy, aah-m appy.'

'Yes, I'm happy and ... yes, I'd like to accept.' I nodded and smiled as I suddenly perspired. That was the quickest and most informal interview I had ever had, in my entire life!

'Congratulations.' I smiled again as he reached to shake my hand. Hearing the word 'hired' sounded typically American and bizarre, as we 'hire' cars in the UK, yet people can be hired too!

His voice was unassuming. 'Wh-aale yew are here, aad laake yew to meet with Miss P-yen-rose and she ca-y-n gi-y-ve y'all the books and information yew need. Let's see if we can faand her. Come with me please, Mr Woo-ood.'

I followed him, courteously. It was as if every step he took was slow and calculated just like his speech. As we walked down a wide corridor, I looked at the shiny blue lockers on both sides. Everything was gleaming, including the floors, and this school really looked 'all American'.

We entered Miss Penrose's classroom and saw her sitting at a computer, busily working, on the far side of the room.

'Miss P-yen-rose. Aad laa-ke to introduce yew to Mr Woo-ood. He will be joining us when school starts.' She slowly looked round, smiled, stood up and walked towards me.

'Hey! Pleased to meet yew.' She energetically put out her hand to

91

shake mine. She had short blonde hair, wore metal-framed glasses, had blue eyes and wore minimal make-up. She was pretty, about five-foot five and a little over weight. Looking smart, she wore dark trousers and a blouse.

'This is Pauuul Woo-ood, and he will be teachin' scaa-ence and ma-y-th. Would it be okay if aah l-y-eft him with yew and yew ca-yn talk him through everythin' that he needs?' I was getting used to the word math and wondered why we called it 'maths'.

'Of course.' She winked at him and smiled at me. The principal quietly left the room. 'It's nice to meet yew!' she said cheerfully.

'It's nice to meet you, too!' We talked at ease, for several minutes mainly about 'math' and she gave me a textbook weighing in at three tonnes and a pack of workbooks that would look better in a library. I noticed her dialect sounded faster and sharper.

'To be honest, I thought I would be teaching just science. Math is not really my subject.'

'I'm sure you will be faane.' She continued smiling and had a comical and infectious laugh that put me at ease straight away. Within minutes, she handed me the math textbook.

'Has this got all the answers in it?' I asked as I smiled.

'Haha! Believe me, it is not all tha-y-t baad', she giggled. 'So, yew are from inglaand, then?'

'Yes I am.'

'How naace, which part?'

'I lived in London, but I'm originally from a small town near Manchester. Have you heard of Manchester?'

'I thi-y-nk I have. Is that where Manchester United is?'

'You have heard of it! How long have you worked in this school?'

'Faave years. Have yew been teaching long?'

'About eight years. Too long!' I laughed.

'I know what you mean. The ke-ey-ds are going love your accent!'

She laughed a few more times and I warmed to her quickly as she seemed funny and approachable.

'I had bed-der take you to meet Pa-y-t. She teaches scaa-ence and she will run through everythin' with yew. Look, do you want my email add-re-yss, then you can contact me if yew ha-y-ve any questions?'

She quickly wrote down her email address.

'Thanks Hayley.'

'Pa-y-t is naace. She will help yew a lot.'

Pat was older, maybe in her fifties, of small stature and seemed quite robust. She also had blonde hair, wore a checked shirt and jeans and her southern accent was stronger than Hayley's. The science textbook was even heavier and older than the math textbook that Hayley gave me. She also gave me two other workbooks, and a folder containing transparencies that I could show to the students using an over-head projector! My pile of books was growing taller and getting heavier by the minute. I think a pick-up truck would have come in handy right at that moment. The textbook looked like something out of the 1970s and some of the pages had stuck together. It seemed I was teaching Earth sciences as the topics included geology and oceanography.

'Yew wi-y-ll be teachin' the-y-m evolution at some point. Now, tha-y-t maaght be a problem for some of these ki-ey-ds, as they don't believe in evolution. As yew know, many are Christians, here. Are yew Christian?' It was a rather personal question to ask me, as she had only just met me; nevertheless, I answered her.

'Yes, and I still teach it, but I understand you don't necessarily have to believe it. Evolution is just a theory, and I always emphasise that. I will be careful teaching this topic, don't worry.'

'We-y-ll, if yew ha-y-ve any problems, just holler.'

'Does that mean, give you a shout?'

'Yer Bri-dish, right? Yew wi-y-ll get used to us!' She laughed again. I think I was going to like her too but she was more matter of fact than Hayley.

'Thank you, Pat.'

'Aah wi-y-ll talk to yew more on training day. We wi-y-ll get plenty of taame, don't worry! Aah wi-y-ll take yew back to Hayley.'

As we walked down the corridor, she stopped in her tracks. 'So, do yew ha-y-ve a place to live?'

'I'm hoping to get that sorted soon, thanks for asking.'

'Aah have a few things at home that I don't want, so if yew need anything just holler.'

'Thank you, Pat.'

'My da-y-d daaed a few months ago.'

'Oh ...' I looked at her, feeling confused. 'I'm sorry to hear that.' It seemed a rather personal statement in the little time we had known each other.

'It's okay. It's just tha-y-t he was about yer saaze. Aah ha-y-ve a paale of shirts that I was going to gi-y-ve away. Aah-ll bring the-y-m in for yew tomorrow, if yew wa-y-nt the-y-m?'

'Oh, right ... thank you!' I did not know what to say. We had arrived back at Hayley's room during this part of the conversation and Hayley looked over as Pat mentioned the kind offer of her dad's shirts. Hayley and I looked at each other with blank expressions.

'Aah-ll ca-y-tch yew lay-der, Pauuul. Please let me know if there is anything yew need.'

As Pat left the room, Hayley started laughing again, it was such an infectious laugh, and we both sat down at the students' desks.

'We-y-ll, at least yew won't run out of shirts!'

'I don't know how I feel about wearing a dead man's shirts!'

'Aahm just pick-in wid ya.'

'Pickin?'

'It means teasin.'

'Oh ... I'm learnin.' She giggled, as I tried to speak in drawl. Hayley then walked me to the classroom I would be using.

'You could play football in here! I mean soccer. It's huge!' I remarked.

'I know, it is the biggest room in the hall! In fa-y-ct, I think it is the biggest classroom in this da-y-mn school!'

She giggled again. Her giggles and laughter were so contagious that every time she cracked a joke, I just laughed even more, sometimes quite uncontrollably. She seemed to see the funny side of everything; I was looking forward to working with her.

'Yew can cha-y-nge it round, if yew wi-y-sh, but that is up to yew.'

As we entered the classroom, there was a high bench immediately to my left and the students' desks were typically American. The chairs were made of wood, and fixed to these were the desks that rotated and flipped up to allow the students to get out of the chairs. There were around thirty of them packed into the room and at the front was a big teacher's desk. It looked retro and weighty, made of wood and solid steel. Behind this was a white board, covering the entire front wall, and at one end was a pull-down map. I rolled down both maps: a world map and inside it, a map of America. Positioned above was an American flag and in the corner of the room, near the white board, was an illuminated deep glass cabinet. Everything looked 'American' and the room was twice the size of a normal classroom in the UK.

After spending over two hours in the school, I said my goodbyes to the teachers I had met and carried a mountain of books back to my car, placing them in the boot. I looked back at the school and paused: this was indeed the dawn of a new chapter.

I got into my car and thought about things for a few minutes, looking around at the school. The American 'jigsaw puzzle' was fitting together: I now had a job and a car. My next challenge was to find somewhere to live.

16

Before driving back to the motel, I decided to have a quick scout around Micro – my new local town. There was not that much to explore; in fact, it was more of a ghost town and I expected tumbleweed to roll past me as the wind stirred.

I could fully appreciate why they had named this town 'Micro'. It was, indeed, tiny and there appeared to be nothing there apart from a school, a store, a small wooden chapel and a desolate railway crossing, although I had not fully looked around. Micro was near the exit of the Interstate 95 (I-95) – ideal for quick get-a-ways. However, curiosity got the better of me, and while I was there, I wanted to go into its local store – seemingly Micro's only shop!

I really felt like buying some cigarettes and I also needed to buy a box of matches, plus some margarine, of all things. After parking the car, I entered the dimly lit small store, ready to shop for my strange threesome of provisions.

Everything inside seemed neatly packaged: meats, soaps, squishy cheeses and strangely named jars of coffee and biscuits dominated the shelves.

I continued to look around despite being the only person shopping, except three men standing at the checkout, and on first impression, everything seemed 'quaint', even by American standards.

I secretly smiled and the more I thought about it, the more I wanted to smoke a cigarette, although I was hesitant to ask for a packet of 'fags'!

For what seemed like an eternity, I searched around for margarine until I had to submit, calmly walking over to the checkout where the three men were still standing and talking. Two men stood, and one sat on a chair at the till.

As I approached, all three stopped talking, looked at me and stared.

I cleared my throat and in my finest British accent, I asked, 'Excuse me, do you sell matches and margarine, please?'

All three looked at me blankly, blinked in unison and then murmured something that I could not hear nor comprehend.

The man at the checkout spoke first, as he raised his eyebrows: 'What is it tha-y-t yew wa-ÿ-nt?'

'I'd like to buy some matches and margarine, please.'

For some reason, an episode of the *Mr Men* entered my mind, when *Mr Noisy* walked into his local butchers, asking loudly for a 'piece of meat', as the butcher looked at him curiously for ten seconds of over-exaggerated blinking before answering him.

I paused, realising they might not have heard the word 'margarine' before. I repeated my question with trepidation.

'I'd like to buy some matches and ... butter, please.'

'Ex-c-use me?'

Again, they all looked at each other.

'What is, matches?' He tried imitating the way I pronounced matches, without a southern drawl, as if I was talking in another language.

They looked at each other once again, shrugging their shoulders and looking baffled.

'Never mind. Do you sell butter? I repeated myself emphasising butter as '*bu-dd-er*', slowing down my speech one hundred times.

As I waited, I looked in turn at these three men. They must have all been in their mid-twenties and one was over six-foot seven, slim and cross-eyed, dressed in an untucked red checked shirt and muddy dungarees, as if he had been driving a horse plough out in the cornfields on the set of *Little House on the Prairie*.

I had heard rumours of inbred people in North Carolina and maybe this was my first experience of meeting one, or possibly, all three!

The tall one looked at me again, still cross-eyed, smiling gormlessly and exposing a set of teeth that looked more like a set of used spark plugs sticking out of a bonnet-less car in a scrap yard in the pouring rain.

I began feeling slightly uneasy about this situation, as maybe they were all extras in some kind of strange Stephen King movie, set in the outback of Johnston County, and I was about to be brutally murdered. I started to think, 'Shit, I hope I get out of here alive.' I stood there, however, looking at them, determined to buy cigarettes, matches and butter, and swallowed nervously before my dying wish.

'I am looking for, *bu-dd-er*.' This time I reshaped my mouth to a distorted and overemphasised 'O' shape that hurt my face, while miming the spreading of butter with an imaginary knife, onto an imaginary slice of bread.

Suddenly the tall gormless one, smiled broadly, jumped up and down several times and pointed at me shouting 'SP-RE-YEAD!'

'Yes, sp-re-yead!' I nodded nervously.

I broke out in a sweat, at this point, thinking he might have a shotgun underneath the till and wanted to blow my head clean off, just for the hell of it. Foolishly, I continued with my game of charades, which stupidly and quickly developed into full role-play, as I mimed striking an invisible match and lighting an imaginary cigarette, pretending to puff out smoke like some 1940s Hollywood movie star.

He shouted again, this time, twitching and frothing at the mouth, showering me with a pint of fresh saliva.

'HE MEANS MAA-TCH-ES, MAA-TCH-ES!'

He laughed for the most uncomfortable minute of my life and, gradually, I forced a lopsided smile while carefully watching his hands, just in case he reached for that sawn-off shotgun.

I wanted to smile, applaud loudly yet urinate myself. From now on, all I had to do was play charades with the local people!

My communication skills were now in full swing, yet I was feeling more uneasy every passing second and was half-expecting to hear the music to *Countdown* (a British game show), followed by the bang of a shooting rifle instead of the famous gong noise.

Quietly sighing with relief, hoping they would not notice me slowly backing away, I glanced sideways noticing the biggest pig's head I had ever seen, placed on the top of a rusty chest freezer. Firstly, I thought nothing of it and then looked back again as if it was an everyday occurrence. I looked back, I was right, it was a pig's head – in fact, it was genetically super-sized, with one eye wide open and staring right at me and the other eye closed, with a big grin on its face. The pig was winking at me and I was half-expecting it to say, in southern drawl, 'You're next, bud!'

I felt like squealing too, like the pig once had, as my jaw dropped to the floor and I moved back, banging into some kind of freestanding metal shelving system, knocking every loaf of bread off onto the floor.

'WHAT THE ...', I shouted, backing off as I recoiled in horror, pointed and stared in complete disbelief.

'WHA-Y-T?' they all shouted back at me.

'THAT, THAT ... PIG'S HEAD? WHAT THE FUCK!' I was ready to shit myself too!

This situation was now beyond a joke and, suddenly I had a vision: my head placed next to the supersized pig's head with matching smiles as I winked, with writing across my forehead saying 'all the way from England'.

The halfwit sitting at the checkout started laughing like some kind of village idiot, with his teeth sticking out in all directions. He either had too many chromosomes or all of them were missing, and all I wanted was to run off down the I-95.

'It's come from a hog roast. Folks baah 'em an' boil 'em!' They all laughed again, this time more disturbingly, just like the sinister laughing clown at Blackpool Pleasure Beach, and this time, the seated man was falling out of the checkout chair.

My mouth was dry, and after placing a five-dollar bill on the counter, I slowly walked backwards and nervously said, 'Keep ... the ... change.'

'Thank-ya', he said, exposing those pearly white teeth.

'I'm sorry about the ... bread.'

My eyes darted side to side at their staring faces and at the grinning and winking, pig, as I slowly backed out of the store bumping into another shelf.

I broke into the fastest sprint humanly possible, clumsily and hurriedly turned on the ignition, literally wheel spinning to the exit of the I-95 – 'that quick get-away'. That was indeed, the most defining moment of my North Carolinian experience so far.

I arrived back at the motel in record time and by the grace of God, I had managed not to deficate myself. Walking to my room and breathing erratically, all I wanted to do was lie down for the rest of the day was smoke weed and not cigarettes.

As I placed the key in the lock, I noticed a note stuck to the door.

Meet me at those apartments in Clayton? I am there now ... Ade ☺

17

Ade and Hazel (the housing-complex manager) were literally crying with laughter as I recounted my 'pig story' and then Ade introduced me to Hazel. She was in her early twenties, sported short blonde hair, blue eyes and looked very pretty. She was a single mum who lived at the complex.

As we walked around, Ade made intermittent pig noises, making us laugh several times. Hazel showed us two different empty one-bedroomed apartments, which had living rooms the size of tennis courts, huge fridge freezers (with icemakers), cookers (stoves) and industrial-sized dishwashers. Deep-pile cream carpets ran through each room and each apartment had a small balcony – the ultimate luxury! I preferred the apartment on the first floor as the balcony overlooked a woodland area behind the complex rather than the car park. No complex would be complete without its own private open-air heated swimming pool, small gymnasium and Internet room!

Ade decided to take the apartment downstairs and after agreeing and signing the paperwork, we grinned smugly and the apartments were officially ours – mission completed!

I quickly looked up at Ade.

'Now we are living the American dream: a home, a job and a car all in one week!'

'Maybe the streets are paved with gold here, after all', he replied.

Barely a week ago, we had nothing to our name and were feeling sorry for ourselves, stuck in that backwater motel.

'Hold on mate, I don't have a job yet!' He started giggling again, more nervously this time, as I think he was worried.

'Oh shit, I forgot about that small detail. You will get one tomorrow, probably.' I started laughing.

'The word 'apartment' sounds so 'American'.'

'Shall we load up our 'trunks' with brown paper bags full of food?' I added.

'It's why we are all here, to live the American dream!'

Once I had settled in, I was looking forward to exploring.

Our apartments were a five-minute drive away from an exit onto US Route 70 (US 70). If you calculated your speed at sixty miles per hour, journey times on highways were easy to work out: every one mile took approximately one minute, unless you hit traffic.

I had not experienced much traffic, which was surprising as everyone relied heavily on their cars; roadworks hardly appeared and when you occasionally saw them, they seemed to disappear overnight. Once on the US 70, it took literally twenty minutes to drive to Raleigh and thirty minutes to drive to my new school (in opposite directions). By American standards, these distances were hardly anything but driving these routes on a regular basis meant the miles clocked up quickly. Everyone seemed to drive but if you did walk, it would literally take you a lifetime to get anywhere.

One thing I did notice, however, is that wherever you drive, you are overwhelmed with the amount of open space, making towns and cities in England feel small and crowded in comparison.

After what seemed an eternity of semi-permanent residency at the motel, Ade and I finally moved into our apartments in Clayton. I now had a zip code, and was feeling 'American' – with a British accent!

The new apartment complex was built in red brick that reminded me of houses in England and for the first two nights, I slept on a deep pile carpet – who needs a bed!

The following day, Ade and I ventured into Smithfield to buy everything we needed for our apartments, choosing from massive displays of ex-rental furniture stored in a rundown warehouse. Within ten minutes, we had furnished our entire apartments for less than $1000. I chose simple furniture: two sofas, a coffee table, a dining table with four chairs, a bed (and mattress), a chest of drawers and a bed-side table. The furniture company even threw in a complimentary bedside lamp.

Next-day delivery was only an extra $30, so I left my key with one of the boys (who you had to 'trust'). I would arrive home the following day to a fully furnished, ergonomically styled apartment, including a plumbed-in American-style top loader washing machine, courtesy of the complex manager - they do not mess around in America!

'Well, at least that is all sorted', Ade said and then sighed.

'Yeah, I'm glad we now have homes.'

'Yeah, it's all been a bit stressful.'

'It has.'

'Look, do you fancy getting something to eat?'

'That's a good idea.'

We both drove back to the motel and then Ade offered to drive me in his car. About half an hour later, we drove past a pizza place on Capital Boulevard near downtown Raleigh.

'Let's go back and check out that pizza place we just drove past.'

Ade turned at the next exit and drove back, parking up outside the pizza place. We both looked at the sign, 'All you can eat for $5'.

'We have got to go in there!' I said, as Ade laughed.

As we walked across, I noticed a view of Raleigh. I had not spent much time in Raleigh and, on first impression, its empty streets seem to lack human existence.

Strangely, I liked its bleakness, but I needed to explore it. I am sure it had interesting places to eat and upmarket restaurants. I had eaten all types of food in my time and I had a wide taste but an eating experience was about to happen, and one I would never forget.

Inside, and once seated, we could eat pizza, pasta and salad to our hearts' content for only five dollars. We certainly had our fair share, and as we tucked in to our fifth piece of super-sized pizza, we watched a family of four (I presumed mum, dad and two sons) devouring everything in sight, like it was the end of the world. They all must have collectively weighed the same as an African elephant and certainly had an appetite like one. They were all uncomfortably squashed in to their chairs, looking like they had been forced in them and would have to be prised out, once they had finished eating. In the middle of their small round table, was a pile of paper plates, which literally piled to the ceiling – maybe it was a competition to see who could explode the first.

One hour later, after eating for England and America, I looked at Ade who just sat there, with a glazed expression on his reddened face and then he lay his forehead on the table, and uttered, 'I'm gonna die.'

18

After spending time organising my apartment and seeing Ade over the last few days, I wanted to drive to Charlotte that weekend, alone, just to unwind. I had read on the internet it was worth visiting, especially an area named SouthPark, which had a large shopping mall. I had read that people who reside in Charlotte are referred to as 'Charlotteans' and I was especially looking forward to experiencing its humid subtropical climate.

Saturday morning arrived and it was bright and sunny. I drove and just, drove. Different signs to different places on the highways and interstates said 105 MILES, 127 MILES, 108 MILES, nothing seemed to be said in two numbers. There seemed to be so much space yet I felt relaxed in its emptiness, as I drove my Mirage, listening to quiet music while cruising at a constant speed of around sixty miles per hour, and those wide roads, it just felt as if I was driving slowly. I noticed a square black and white sign with '70' written on it and experienced elation. Gradually, and unknowingly, I increased my speed, but it wasn't too long before a white saloon was tailgating me. However, I was none the wiser and carried on driving.

'Overtake me, you idiot', I blurted out, as I looked at the white car that remained close behind me.

I looked in my rear-view mirror again, whispering the word 'prick', defensively gaining speed trying to get away from him, when suddenly, blue lights started flashing inside his windscreen.

'SHIT!'

The unmarked police car quickly pulled me over and within seconds I stopped and the white car parked behind me with its blue lights still flashing. The police officer remained in his car for what seemed an eternity.

As I opened the door, a loud robotic-sounding North Carolinian voice blurted out from a speaker on the car:

'PL-EA-SE REMAIN IN YER VE-AR-CAL!'

I froze and the Earth rotated once before anything else happened.

Another loud voice boomed from his car. Maybe it was on a go-slow timer? 'PL-EA-SE REMAIN IN YER VE-AR-CAL!'

An extremely short and overweight police officer, slowly waddled over – I had never seen a person with these bodily dimensions before. He looked like a small bull. I pressed the electric window button while staring at him in complete disbelief.

'Is th-y-s yer ve-ar-cal, sir?'

Tempted to say 'no', just to witness his reaction, I thought it would be a better idea to do whatever he said. I was sure sarcasm would not go down well at that precise moment, so I looked up with puppy-dog eyes before quietly responding.

'Yes, it is, sir.'

He immediately spoke on his radio and talking in a strong accent, beyond comprehension, repeated the licence plate number several times, while looking at me as if I had killed seven people on my journey.

'Do yer rea-l-aase tha-y-t yer were draa-ving a-y-t sev-endy-si-y-x maales a-y-n hour?'

I continued staring at him, and after several seconds of trying to understand him, I responded in an overly pronounced British accent: a bizarre fusion of a jittery Hugh Grant and a posh Liz Hurley.

'I'm sorry, sir. I actually did not realise the speed limit – I thought it was seventy.'

'No sir, only on certain se-a-c-tions of the uuu-eess sev-endy, but not th-i-ys se-a-ction, on th-y-is se-a-ction of the ind-er-state, it is si-y-xty. It does not mean yew ca-y-n draave at sev-endy on th-y-is se-a-c-shan. Thi-y-is is the 'eye sev-en-dy.'

Looking at him with a glazed expression for what seemed to be several minutes, I suddenly thought what I had seen was a sign for the Interstate 70, not seventy miles per hour. In response, I cupped my head with both hands and lay my forehead on the steering wheel for a few seconds.

'What an idiot!'

'So-rr-y?' he forcefully said.

'I mean, I'm such an idiot, I was … really confused, sir … officer. I have just moved from England and I thought the seventy-sign meant you could drive at seventy. This is the first time I have driven outside of Clayton.'

'Sir, dew yew ha-y-ve yer draa-ver's laa-cense?' Maybe he thought I did just kill seven people and, maybe, he thought I had stolen this car too! I was digging myself in deeper by the minute.

'I do have one', I said, as I reached for the glove compartment.

'NO SIR!'

I was about to open it.

'ST-Y-OP!' he yelled louder.

'WHAT DID I DO?' I felt pains in my chest.

'GIT OUT OF YER VE-AR-CAL!' Now I actually felt like a mass murderer! This was indeed a new-found hurdle and was getting more ludicrous by the second.

'STA-Y-ND AWAY FROM YER VE-AR-CAL!' That was not a polite request but an order.

'Sir, this is my first time driving long distance on the highway, I mean interstate ... highway ... interstate.' I stopped speaking, stared at him, sighed and bowed my head. He probably thought I was high on drugs. (My jittery Hugh Grant accent now sounded utterly ridiculous.) I had only been in the USA for a few days but thought I might even go to jail. How am I going to explain this to school, VIF... my dad?

I looked down and said quietly, 'I want to go home', and as he made me stand by the car, I decided to stay quiet.

'Sir, ahh need t'make another c-aa-ll a-y-nd che-y-ck thi-y-s is yer ve-ar-cal. Is yer draa-ver's laa- cense in yer glo-y-ve box?' This was a man – obsessed!

'What?' I now found it difficult to translate anything.

'Aah rep-eet, is yer draa-ver's laa-cense in yer glo-y-ve box?' he asked again, sounding annoyed. I suddenly worked out that he was talking about the glove compartment.

'YES SIR!' I responded like an army recruit and saluted him as a stood to attention!

He slowly walked around the vehicle suspiciously inspecting it and then looked in the glove compartment to find my licence. This situation was turning into some type of Monty Python sketch (comical – but I really was not in the mood to laugh). Within minutes, he walked

107

back around the car and spoke to me still saluting him on the busy highway.

'Sir, th-y-s also appears to be the wrong laa-cense plate on yer ve-ar-cal.'

'What?' I scratched my head in confusion and thought this could not get any worse.

'Sir, yer were draa-vin' at an exc-e-ss speed aav se-v-enty-si-x maa-les per ho-w-ur. Yer do not a- ve to saan th-y-is form, b-u-t if yer doo, yew have to pay a faane, or if yew w-i-y-sh to app-eel, the-y-n yer may complete the baa-ck of the form and att-ind court.'

Now, his southern drawl would have been more fitting in a scene from *Star Wars* (when aliens from different planets meet at an intergalactic cafe). Not only did it take him an eternity to say that to me, I definitely needed a lawyer and a translator and I really did not want to ask him to repeat all of that again just in case he decided to handcuff me and take me to the nearest jail.

It was hot and I had been standing for over an hour still saluting him on the side of interstate with cars whooshing past at what seemed like 'an exc-ess aav se-ve-nty-si-x maales per ho-ur'. I looked at him again with big puppy dogs' eyes, hoping that might just do the trick, but did not make the slightest difference. This man was on a mission and all I really wanted to say was 'Ha-y-ve a naace d-ay.' I sighed and took the ticket.

'Please draave safely, sir', were his last words as he slowly wobbled away and prised himself back into the driver's seat of his gleaming white undercover cop car, which suddenly slumped all down the left side followed by mysterious jerking up and down movements that nearly broke the suspension. I really thought all four wheels were going buckle out sideways.

He then stared at me nodding curiously for several minutes before 'appearing' to do some more paper work – he was probably writing down that I was a complete asshole.

That was my first experience of meeting someone of a whalelike proportion and utterly stupid – and it was beyond me how he would be able to outrun a criminal!

I got back into my car, sighed heavily and laid my head back into the headrest and blurted out, 'I need a drink.' I had not been in the country for two minutes, and now this.

I was feeling too scared to drive off, just in case he tailed me again. He turned the flashing lights off in his humongous unmarked police car – he obviously had minute genitalia.

I waited several minutes until the fear of driving on the interstate again had subsided, patiently waiting for a gap in the busy traffic, and then I quickly accelerated away. The engine whined loudly, moving through each gear automatically with the high revs as I pressed the accelerator pedal right down to the floor. The last thing I needed was someone crashing into the back of me and I quickly reached a cruising speed of sixty. I was damned if I was going to travel any faster, although it still seemed like every other driver still was.

After that humiliating experience, I decided to turn back at the next exit to spend the rest of the afternoon in Walmart.

19

I was always led to believe our solar system had nine planets but as soon as I walked through the main entrance of Walmart, that theory went straight out of the window – I had entered 'Walmart world'- a new dimension!

The large number of people using mobility scooters shocked me; the scooters were transporting the biggest people I had ever seen, weighing in at fifty stone at least, so they must have had turbo charged engines. Within this 'Walmart world' lived 'Walmart people'; this was indeed, another planet.

Once inside, you could register with an optician, have your hair cut, let your children play in a glass box full of soft bouncy coloured balls and as you waited to have your car serviced, you could buy groceries! The only thing missing was a river running through the middle of it – then I could pitch a tent in aisle 21, and live there forever. I had never seen anything like it! Not even the grossly oversized hypermarkets in Calais compared to this.

Walmart sold anything and everything you could possibly imagine: from roses to rifles! In fact, one rifle was on sale, a 'bargain' at a mere $350, and I wondered how easy it would be to buy one. Imagine your shopping list: 3 onions, 1 loaf of bread, 2 tins of tuna...oh erm, and 1 shotgun.

I spent the best part of half an hour just in the dairy aisle, gazing at the different varieties of milk – seemingly an endless choice. We are so 'hard done by' in England (just three measly varieties) but the monstrous refrigerated units (each one a mile in length) were stocked with different types of milk, enough to cure every child in the world of Kwashiorkor.

These varieties included: 0% fat-free milk, 1% fat-free milk, 2% fat-free milk, low-fat milk, vitamin D enriched milk, vitamin E enriched milk, chocolate milk and 1% fat-free chocolate milk, all served in quarts, a measurement I was not familiar with. A quart is a quarter of a gallon or two pints, although it looked bigger and seemed cheap at $2 for a quarter of a gallon of milk! Not to mention cartons and over-sized pouches of coconut milk, strawberry low-fat milk, almond milk, goat's milk, lactose-free milk, goat's milk with vitamin D and 'muscle milk' (I assume for body builders?) all served in quarts too. A quart would have probably lasted me a month or so if it could remain fresh!

I looked further down the mile-long aisle but at that point, the glass cabinets on both sides paled into oblivion and I entered a dream-like state of mind. Thinking about which milk to buy was giving me a headache yet I was becoming strangely infatuated with this place. It was evident that you really can have anything you want in this country, and I thought maybe I should visit an aisle each day for the rest of my life.

Apart from my recent encounter with that unmarked police car which nearly rammed me on the 'eye sev-en-dy', and my 'Walmart-world' experience, I spent the rest of the evening lying on my bed with my hands behind my head, staring at the ceiling, feeling sorry for myself. I started thinking about the things I did not have any more: my life in the UK, that 'lush' sports car (as Halise had once described it), my flat, British soap operas, family, friends and all the things I could do in London.

I felt isolated and it had been disheartening waiting around for all those phone calls. Ade still did not have a job and now looked like he had been lobotomised. I think he was about ready to turn into a kamikaze car driver at any given moment on the nearest highway, just to end his 'suffering' – and mine also at one point! Recently, he drove me in his car around a sharp bend, as he shouted, 'I'M GOING TO KILL US!'

In comparison, I guess I was 'lucky': at least, now, I had a job but it was still early days.

Some of the teachers employed in some schools were from Columbia and the Philippines, and could hardly speak English, yet many of the Americans had real trouble understanding my British accent! I had no idea how they would get on!

Meanwhile, my North Carolinian vocabulary had expanded and I was learning new words such as: creamer = carton of milk; spread =

margarine/butter; silverware = cutlery; shag = dance (I liked that one); y'all = you all (makes me chuckle every time I hear it); stoplight = traffic light; interstate = motorway between states; highway = motorway within a state; and circle = roundabout.

That night, I dreamt about a 200-mile-long milk isle on '*Planet Walmart*'.

20

The following morning was eventful; our usual crowd needed to meet at Smithfield District Office by 9 a.m. for two hours of form filling, and we were given more letters explaining when we would receive our first pay cheques.

We also had our fingerprints taken and scanned (normal here for teachers) at the county jail. One prisoner walked past me, escorted by a prison guard and said 'howdy' while winking as if he wanted me to be his 'bitch'. He had a skinhead and donned a bright orange boiler suit with shackled ankles – very different to some of the laid-back snooker-playing British prisoners I have heard of who relax on a bed with one hand down the front of their joggers, skilfully texting their pregnant girlfriends with the other, while puffing on a huge joint and watching football on satellite TV – talk about multi-tasking!

Later that afternoon, I visited the library in Smithfield: a small, plain and featureless building. Opposite the reception desk, on a big table positioned in the middle of the room, were several computers. I managed to get a seat; it was time to send my first email home. I left my bag on the seat and walked over to the reception desk, waiting patiently for an elderly woman to serve me.

'Ca-yn ahh help yew?' she asked.

'Hello. Could I please use the Internet?'

The librarian looked in her eighties, and was small, with grey hair and a sweet smile. She softly replied, 'Of course yew ca-yn. Here is ticket faave. Yew ca-yn use the Internet for thir-dy minutes. If yew want more tame, just a-y-sk.'

'Thank you.'

I sat down at the computer and started to type my first email, losing track of time. A warning sign suddenly flashed up on the screen stating I had just five minutes left. I was still in the middle of writing my email, so I got up and walked back to the desk. She looked at me and knew what I was going to ask. 'Yew want more taame?' Before I had chance to answer, she pressed a few buttons on the computer (techno gran!) and gave me a new ticket.

'… thank you!'

'Are yew Brid-ish?'

'Yes.' Now everybody in the library knew.

'Are yew on vacation?' She was inquisitive!

'No, I work here as a teacher.'

'Are yew enjoying it?'

'I haven't started my new job yet.'

'How long have yew been in the States?'

'About a fortnight'

'What is a fort–night?'

'A fortnight?'

'I never heard that word before.' She genuinely did not know and still looked confused.

'Really? It means two weeks. I just keep thinking in British-English. I am going to have to be more aware of what I am saying.'

'Th-y-at must be difficult. St-iy-ll, I never heard th-y-at word before! I gu-y-ess that works both ways. I hope yew enjoy teaching our kids though and I'm sure they will teach yew many American words.'

She started to laugh (in that sweet old-lady style with a high-pitched giggle) reminding me of Jessica Tandy complete with blue twinkly eyes and even the same hairstyle.

'Maybe yew c-y-an educate the-y-m with some of those quaint Bri-dish words?'

She had looked and sounded stern minutes earlier, but now she had a warm smile on her face and had opened up about herself and the way of life there in just a very short space of time, which was a general trait I had noticed. People in North Carolina were open, honest and sociable. I had once viewed Americans as direct and loud but my opinion was changing and what I liked, and appreciated the most, was their manner – they always seemed genuinely interested in you and your background.

Maybe it was their Southern Belle charm. Then again, I had only been to New York and Boston before, and people are always very different in cities.

'So, where have yew been so far during your stay here?' She asked several questions forgetting she was working in a library (supposedly a place of quietness) but she was genuinely interested, in a gentle way. This situation also reminded me of the man I had met when I had arrived at the airport in Atlanta: completely intuitive and endlessly curious.

'I have been staying in a motel in Smithfield for a few days, but I have just moved into a rented apartment in Clayton.'

'H-ave yew been to any places around here y-et?'

'I went to Walmart yesterday for the first time!' She laughed at my response. 'I can't believe you can buy guns there?'

'Aah have one under my b-ed.' She looked deadly serious. 'Oh yeah, if an intruder comes into my house, I'll shoot him.' She relaxed and smiled again – you would not want to cross this grandmother!

I just thought she was just a quiet librarian, not a trained shooter. I could not imagine a woman of her age being a crack-shot with a rifle and it was worrying that she thought it was her 'right' to shoot someone.

'Well, I had better get on and use the computer.' I smiled as I quickly took the ticket from her hand and imagined Jessica Tandy with a firearm. 'Thank you.'

I returned to the computer and continued to write my email.

31 July

Hi y'all. I arrived ok. Had a bit of a shaky start as it took time to get organised finding a place to live and finding a school, so at one point I thought this was never going to work out and thought I'd be coming back home with my tail between my legs. All's well that ends well. Finally, I start my first day in my new school tomorrow. It is a training day so will meet all the new teachers. I will meet the kids next week.

I have gone from zero to hero in a matter of days as I have a job, an apartment and a car (in British racing green – the irony eh?). I really am living and breathing the American dream! My apartment is big and is in a complex called Amelia Village in Clayton. Everyone here is friendly and I have made some friends with other teachers on

115

the teaching programme. I am living upstairs from another English guy, who I get on well with, so I don't feel too much of a loner.

I am presently in Smithfield (in Johnston County, North Carolina). There is not much here, but then again, I have not really explored this area too much.

I've been into Walmart and they seem to sell anything you could possibly want. I had my first experience of gun culture there; I am ok, but saw firearms for sale in a glass cabinet – so much choice! I am emailing you from the library, and was just talking to an elderly librarian. First impression, she's a sweet old woman but guess what, she has a rifle that she keeps under her bed, in case of intruders! It is the American way!

Once I have these two training days out of the way, I am going to venture into Raleigh at the weekend and see what's about.

I will keep you posted on what happens at school tomorrow. If I get time, I will try to come down to the library again and see if 'Gunshot Grannie' will give me another ticket so I can write you another email before the weekend.

The accent is quite difficult to understand but I'm slowly getting used to it. Apart from that, all is good here. I hope that my next email will be a bit meatier once I have done more stuff and settled in a bit.

Lader... P x

After sending my email and waving goodbye to 'Gunshot Grannie', I drove back to Clayton.

I still had nothing to cook with, so I stopped off at McDonald's. Fast food was seriously becoming a bad habit.

21

August 2003

I woke at around 6 a.m. after a poor night's sleep staring at the ceiling, thinking of a good icebreaker for the day ahead. I still had no food in, not even milk from the mile-long dairy aisle, and I knew breakfast would come from the shop at the local petrol station, as I needed fuel. Following two days of casual dress at school during my planning days, I decided to wear chinos and a shirt on the day I met all the staff. At around 7 a.m., I walked over to my car thinking about my new 'American life'.

I tried to quietly pronounce 'g'yas' several times as I filled up the tank, costing a mere $25, and I liked the idea of inserting a debit card into the petrol pump, thereby avoiding the need for any queuing, walking or talking - Americans seemed ahead of the game.

It sounded strange using the word 'gas' – an expression I had only heard on American TV programmes – but now this was a reality. To me, the word meant a gas, not a liquid, and it seemed odd that petrol was sold in gallons, but then again, I could never fully understand why petrol is sold in litres in the UK – maybe it gives us Brits the impression it is cheaper.

Most people around me paid at the pump and then drove off. Maybe queuing is a British thing but I needed to buy breakfast, which ended up being a squishy beef paste sandwich wrapped in cling film and a polystyrene cup filled with a liquid tasting something like tea.

As I walked back to my car, the early morning sunrise was already warming the air and I noticed a small white van in front of me. As I got into my car and sipped my tea before I drove off, a sudden gust of wind caused the van's back doors to swing wide open, exposing numerous Mexican men crammed together and wearing overalls splashed in paint: a van full of cheap manual labour?

I drove off, heading onto US 70 towards my school, consuming my tasteless sandwich and drinking the weak tea en route. Thirty minutes later, I arrived at my school and parked my car around the back.

As I got out of my car, I took my small rucksack out of the boot, then I locked the car and started walking towards the back exit of the school. Suddenly, I noticed Allison getting out of her car too.

'Hey!' I shouted. She looked around, waved and stopped as I caught up with her. 'Do you feel nervous?' I asked.

'A bit. It is nice that we are working at the same school.'

'Yeah, it is.'

'How's Andy? Where is he teaching?'

'Oh, he's really happy and couldn't wait to start school this morning. He's working in a high school not far from here.'

Again, I thought it must be nice for a couple to share this experience and all the uncertainties of working in another country.

'What about Ade, did he get into a school?'

'Yeah, he found out yesterday. He's got a job teaching history, at another good middle school, so he is happy enough.'

'So, we are all sorted with jobs, homes and cars!'

'I know, glad it's all sorted now', Allison stated.

We entered the door of the school and walked down a long corridor towards the main hall. The corridor was gleaming, ready for the new semester. I looked at the lines of blue lockers again as we walked past.

The reception area was laid out with chairs in neat rows facing a large screen, and I sat next to Allison. It was not long before the reception area was full of noise: laughter, smiling faces, people walking around, some of them gesticulating with each other, and everyone looked happy after their summer holidays.

Teachers were casually dressed, mainly in shorts, T-shirts and flip-flops on this hot training day. I remembered once being sent home from a school I worked at in London, when I turned up to an inset day dressed in jeans and they thought it looked 'unprofessional'. I wonder what they would have thought now!

Allison and I sat quietly, however, every so often, we were distracted: loud voices, laughter and other people walking around, hearing snippets of different conversations about fishing, hunting, freeways, interstates, someone's grandma dying, Walmart, trailers and children's birthday parties. Each conversation spoken in southern drawl interrupted by howls of laughter. Some conversations seemed amplified as people talked loudly.

I observed the people around me. It was just another inset day that just happened to be in-an American school - and I thought, if I had not been through that break-up, I would not be here seeing or hearing these people. I would not be in this chair right now, peering through a window at the bright blue sky of Johnston County.

These teacher-training days would be going on in all schools within the county and within the other ninety-nine counties across the entire State of North Carolina, which ranks twenty-ninth in size by area, but has the seventh-highest number of counties in the country. Other counties in North Carolina include Mecklenburg, Wake, Durham, Buncombe, Guildford, Orange, Dare, Pitt and Forsyth to name but a few. Johnston County is further divided into districts, as are all the counties.

Every school has its own agenda and policies, yet teachers were all doing the same job - educating young people. So, this was just like the countless other inset days I have attended before, in England. They are pretty much the same, wherever you are.

Haley and Pat arrived, accompanied by a very heavily pregnant woman who sat next to us. 'Hey!' Hayley smiled at us. 'How was your journey th-i-ys mornin'?'

'I made it in thir-dy minutes fl-a-yt.' They all looked at me as I tried to reply in southern drawl and immediately started to laugh.

'Hey! That was pre-ddy good!' Hayley commented and as she giggled, she added, 'Aah prefer your English accent though, Paul!' She pronounced my name in a posh British accent, which quite impressed me.

'This is Cody. She teaches language arts in our hall' (language arts are the equivalent of English lessons). I noticed how massively pregnant she looked. I know Americans do everything bigger but I am sure she had a whole football team inside that bump. Transfixed, I just wanted to touch it to make sure it was real!

'Y-es, aah know aah look bi-y-g.' She smiled as she proudly patted her small mountain.

'When is it due?'

119

'He's dew October fourteenth', she replied precisely. 'Aah'm havin' an elective C-sey-c-tion.'

'It's all planned out and you know the sex too!'

'It has to be pla-y-nned to fit around school. That is wha-yt pregnant women dew here. They pla-y-n their date of delivery and the date they come ba-y-ck to work.'

I just thought there was no element of surprise in this life-changing event. 'How long will you be off work?'

'Twelve weeks.'

'Is that all?'

'Yeah, we don't get paid if we stay off longer, so we have no choice and that's the maximum taame we g-y-et off. How does it work in ingland?'

'Most women have a year off.'

'Aah wanna move to ingland!'

I had worked out there were three halls, composed of 6th, 7th and 8th graders, equivalent to Years 7, 8 and 9 in British schools. This was a middle school, and even though I attended a middle school as a child, they do not have them anymore in the UK.

'Is a hall like a corridor or section of the school then?' I asked curiously.

Cody intervened. 'If yew don't mind me sayin', the school is laak a wh-ee-y-l with three spokes coming away from the hu-ub. Each spoke is laak a h-all. Aah don't know about every school, but most schools ha-yve their own h-all for each year group.' Cody explained it well in her strong accent.

'I just wondered how it worked, that's all.'

'That's okay, aah thi-y-nk that's how it works anyways. We-y-ll, yew won't have to worry about the other two ha-lls as yew will be on our ha-ll all the taame.'

'You should also get your taametable today from the vice principal', Hayley explained.

'Okay.'

The principal slowly walked over, stopping a couple of times to talk to staff on the way to the front of the hall, and once he had everyone's attention, he spoke slowly and quietly explaining the order of the day.

'Aah would laake to intro-duce our new sta-y-ff who have joined us for thi-y-s school year. Miss Le-wis and Mr Woo-ood are from ingland. Would yew both laake to sta-y-nd up, so we c-yan all see yew?' We stood up together and then looked at each other.

'Ladies first!' I said, as I grinned slyly while gesturing towards Allison, generating more background laughter. Allison blushed and spoke quickly.

'I am not Mr Wood.' Everyone laughed and she introduced herself and which subject she was there to teach, then promptly sat down, looked up and smiled as she raised her eyebrows.

'I'm Paul and I am looking forward to working with you all. I am here to teach math and science. Please look after us!' I sat down quickly and heard some background laughter.

'Well done!' Hayley quietly commented as she smiled.

'Shall we give them all a royal wave?' Allison giggled.

It felt good introducing ourselves, especially in a foreign country. Evidently, Allison was feeling confident, as she still had a smile on her face and was looking around, not for admiration but I think for a few seconds she was just as overwhelmed as I was.

'I feel like a celebrity,' I discreetly said to Allison.

'I know what you mean. I feel like everyone is looking at us.'

'Do you think they expect us to look different because we are British?' Allison giggled.

The principal talked further about the day and that we would be in our departments that afternoon. Hayley explained and discreetly 'translated' in her own way as the principal talked about the end of year grades or EOGs, the cohort of the new sixth graders, how pleased he was with their results and how those compared to other middle schools in the county, and how we had an even bigger challenge of trying to raise the target for this academic year.

We stopped for coffee around 11 am and later on we ate a free lunch served in white plastic compartmentalised trays. The food had a gooey texture and a sweetish after-taste. Each piece of food was placed in a separate compartment and was composed of breaded meat, peas, mashed potato and sweet bread, with a small sickly-sweet custard-type yoghurt dessert wrapped in a foiled-packaged carton and placed in the smallest compartment on the tray. All of the food tasted sweet, even the meat! There was also a sugary drink called Gatorade and I chose the lemon flavour, which tasted ten times sweeter. My sugar rush lasted for the rest of the day.

22

My first training day at school passed surprisingly quickly. I had seen my teaching timetable and each day was composed of four 90-minute blocks, with teaching for three of those blocks. The 1st block was teaching science, the second block was free, the third block I would teach the same class math and escort them to lunch, then continue teaching them after lunch. (Thirty kids on sugar-rushes would be interesting). Then, I would teach math, in the 4th block, to a different, more able class, and these would be the ones to test out my 'math' skills!

I had memorised my timetable within minutes, whereas in England, it would take me whole term to remember.

Each teaching block seemed long. I was worried how to keep them occupied, but there was an afternoon break for twenty minutes in the fourth block, easing up some time. Hayley advised me to give the students different activities to keep the lesson varied as much as possible.

I also had to teach a science experiment in a laboratory, when I could, and this was called 'lab' although there were no laboratory technicians, so I had to order and prepare what equipment was available myself – and store them and any chemicals I needed in a cupboard and, hopefully, not blow up the whole school – that could have been one big hurdle!

'They have to study oceanography, in 8th grade?' I had a bad habit of talking to myself. This was a topic I had not taught before in the UK and was more like geography than science.

The second day was also another training day and seemed to go more quickly. I also met two other teachers on my hall, a married couple called Mr and Mrs Barton, who seemed pleasant and held strong Christian values. I had worked with a married teaching couple together previously in England. Mr and Mrs Barton were my age although appeared older, not just in their dress sense but in their views on life and the way they talked, they just seemed, 'grown up!'

Getting to grips with algebra was now my priority. 'I love algebra,

I love algebra', I said quietly as I gritted my teeth.

I tried to practise a few equations, which seemed confusing. I became frustrated, stood up and walked around my large classroom.

Earlier, the vice principal had given out documentation explaining that students would arrive for breakfast around 7.30 a.m., and about 7.55 a.m. students go to their lockers before entering classrooms. At 8 a.m. precisely, all students and teachers pledge their allegiance to the United States. I had placed a copy of the pledge on my desk. Hayley advised me to stand at the side of the room and not say anything. I quickly read the pledge.

'The kids have to say this every day?' I said aloud. They have probably said it at the same time every morning since the moment they could talk. I could not imagine British kids standing up, facing a Union Jack in the corner of their classroom and singing 'Rule, Britannia!' especially in some of the tough inner-city state schools where, no doubt, riots would ensue.

Following the Pledge, the TV would automatically turn on and the kids would watch American news for fifteen minutes, again each day. The first block began at 8.30 a.m. and I was 'strangely' looking forward to experiencing this new regime.

I had always taught in a laboratory and never in a classroom, especially not one as big as this – I felt lost standing at the front and could hardly see the back of the room! I wanted to rearrange my classroom, instead of learning more algebra and began moving the heavy teacher's desk in front of the board.

'That is heavy!' As soon as I started to move it, its metal legs scratched the floor letting out a loud ear-piercing screech. Suddenly, a woman from nowhere seemed to leap 'bionically' into the middle of the classroom.

'WH-Y-AT ARE YEW DOIN'?' she shouted, following her ten-foot leap.

'I'm just moving the furniture around.' I thought she was ready to shoot me!

'Yer scraatching all the floors, young maan!' This woman was angry! She wore a dark green army-style outfit and looked in her mid to late forties; she just happened to be the main janitor and vaguely reminded me of prison warden.

After several minutes of explaining how I wanted to rearrange the room, another, younger janitor quickly entered. She did not say anything, but within seconds, they both started to help me move furniture around as they joked about my startled reaction – working here was going to be 'interesting', to say the least!

It was time to go home and, after collecting my things and saying goodbye to some work colleagues, I left the school. As I walked over to my car in the mid-afternoon heat, heavily laden with books and two small heavy rucksacks that kept falling off each shoulder, I stopped and thought I had better go back inside and practise more algebraic equations.

I walked back, pushing open the metal door with my body and almost bumped into Tabitha (Tee) Alcorn (a young language arts teacher) equally loaded up with her books. She had moved down from New York State following a break up of her relationship and wanted a new start.

She was funny, loud, frank, pretty, had dark brown hair, was in her early twenties and heavily pronounced her r's.

'Do you want some help?' I joked as I looked up at my stack of books.'

'How is that possible, you're a mobile library!' she started laughing. 'You are such an English gentleman! Are you doing more work?'

'Yeah, I've still got loads to do.'

'Are you crazy? Why don't we get something to eat and worry about it tomorrow?'

'Now, that sounds like a good idea! I feel like eating Walmart.'

'You mean eating at Walmart?'

'Oh, yeah! Sorry, I'm tired.'

'Let's go then.'

As I balanced my books, we walked back to the car park and we agreed on driving back to Walmart in Clayton and meeting there. I followed her noticing how confident she seemed as she drove with her left arm casually hanging out of the driver's window, holding a cigarette. Driving an automatic was convenient for any smoker but she made driving look cool and relaxing, as we cruised around sixty most of the way back.

It was hot and the flow of traffic was continuous. I had my windows up and the air conditioning on full for the whole journey. I turned the radio on and some British music was playing. I had a thought that I must buy some music for these long journeys to and from school, if only for the company. Forty minutes later, we pulled up next to each other in the half-empty car park at Walmart.

I pressed the button to open the driver's window and the cool air inside the car quickly dissipated, allowing the oppressive heat to enter rapidly, making me sweat instantly. I wanted to dive into the swimming pool, back at my complex.

'Where do you want to eat?' I asked.

'Shall we go to Arby's?'

'What kind of food is it?'

'It's fast food but tastes good.' I got out of the car.

'Where are you going?' she asked.

'Walking to Arby's?' as I pointed to the nearby sign.

'Really?'

'It's not that far.' Before I had chance to finish speaking, she drove off. She really did not want to walk.

I had noticed, in fact, nobody walks. Everywhere was connected by interstates or freeways and there were no pavements. The only person I had seen 'moving' was Ade jogging, looking peculiar as his white-haired head bobbed up and down – he could be seen from a mile away!

I stood by my decision and walked to meet Tabitha in Arby's, literally five minutes from Walmart.

She stopped her car.

'Get in, Porl!' she almost grabbed me.

Once inside Arby's, there seemed an endless choice of meat sandwiches: roast beef, brisket, turkey, 'Reuben' (corned beef) and Italian meat.

I stared at Tee. 'I have no idea what to eat.'

'I recommend the beef sandwich.'

Once I had ordered the sandwich, with spicy curly fries and a bottle of Mountain Dew, literally one minute later we had both been served and were sitting down with food neatly laid out on our trays.

As I bit into my beef sandwich, the tasty tzatziki sauce oozed in all directions, dripping all over my hands and the table. She was right, I loved it. The entire contents melted in my mouth into a weird texture that could only be described as a sweet and syrupy consistency and I had never tasted anything quite like this before – we British were certainly missing out!

I ate it quickly and instantly had cravings for three more servings. I had also never tried the fizzy drink called Mountain Dew. Indeed, this was a totally new palatable experience and I wanted to pole-vault over the counter and gorge everything in sight.

'Oh my ... God: *Arby's*!' Tabitha laughed, as I emphasised Arby's in a deep silly voice. We walked back to her car and drove over to Walmart, arriving seconds later.

I was still in a frenzy from my 'Arby's experience' and thought a cheeky revisit might have to happen soon.

I looked in sheer amazement at the range of stationery available in Walmart and decided to buy a pack containing what looked like one million pencils, for 99 cents for the kids at school. Everything seemed cheaper here!

We ambled down the music aisle and started browsing through the racks of CDs. They all cost around $10 and I paused, as I noticed *American Life*, by Madonna, and picked it up.

'I have to get this!' I said to Tee, holding the CD in the air.

I had bought Madonna's *Ray of Light* back in the nineties and remembered playing the whole album four hours each way (yes, I loved it), on my journeys to and from London in Phil's car. I often drove late at night when the motorways were clear, listening to the songs while being transfixed by the cat's eyes on the road that seemed to become blurry – then I arrived home in a trance as if I had been meditating, not driving.

'It's supposed to be a good album,' Tabitha confidently affirmed.

After another hour or so of browsing around the ridiculously cheap merchandise that would only end up as clutter, I decided not to buy anything else except for the pack of pencils and the Madonna CD.

We left, said goodbye at the car park and drove home separately.

I inserted the *American Life* album into the car's CD player. Some lyrics seemed apt, relating to how I was feeling and what I was thinking.

'*Do I have to change my name? This type of modern life – is it for me? I live the American dream.*' Inside the confines of my car, I was beginning to experience the American dream.

One part of the lyrics that stood out was, '*Do I have to change my name?*' I could have taken on a new name, as nobody knew me there. I had started a new and very modern American life, one that seemed brash, loud, open, and bright – everything was within reach and driving seemed easy.

As I drove and looked through the windscreen, everywhere looked spacious and tranquil. Life there felt quite the opposite of that in the UK. This new existence in North Carolina was moving me forward - quickly. Just as my car was, on yet another journey, moving me forward. Each old mile disappearing from view was my past life fading away: the disappointments and the pain quickly becoming distant memories. Each new mile I drove was part of my new adventure, a happier me. I would keep driving until I saw that clearer picture and knew I would have to drive many miles, losing myself as I listened to the lyrics of her songs.

I continued driving and familiarising myself with the area as I listened to more of Madonna's music. For several minutes, I was alone on the US 70 – I 'owned' it. Three empty lanes ahead of me invited me in, and as I glanced in rear view mirror, three empty lanes behind me merged into one. My thoughts intensified as I kept on driving. At times, I was lost in thought and did not know who I was, where I was or what I was doing. At that moment, I felt lonely on the big empty highway but, strangely, I enjoyed the solitude. It was just me, my music and the road, and nothing else seemed to matter.

I was lost in my mind and lost on this highway. Each mile I drove would be a mile closer to finding out who I was. This was the beginning of a new journey. It was now time to forget everything: my thoughts, my world, my feelings and my pain.

More lyrics: '*Was I supposed to know who I was? Was I supposed to give a damn? And in the process of thinking, I remembered, I was special too*'. Despite how somebody else had made me feel and how broken I had once felt; those feelings were becoming distant and painless memories – quickly disappearing like the diminishing lanes behind me.

An illuminated sign on the road caught my attention: 'Jesus loves you!' This was indeed the Bible Belt, and although it was the first religious sign I had seen, it prompted me to think. I cynically giggled and whispered, 'Do you?'

God must have known about the journey I was taking and the reasons why I was there. I kept on driving and one mile soon become ten, then ten miles soon became a hundred, yet they all faded into one. Driving thirty or so miles meant nothing and you could quickly forget how far you had travelled just as quickly as you saw the next sign. I looked in my rear-view mirror noticing the 'Jesus' sign rapidly disappearing.

I focused again on the lyrics and I noticed how 'r's' emphasised the words, just like Tabitha's accent, more than any other letter in the alphabet. I had noticed the same emphasis with other people I had met there, especially with their southern drawl, when they said words such as: bar, part, for, more, forever, father, mother, together, car, future, better and girl.

Americans generally rolled their r's, often sounding like there were two r's in words, loosely reminding me of a West Country accent and, in some ways, of Nick's.

A word such as computer was pronounced 'compud-err', and was heavily emphasised within the North Carolinian accent. Although, the American language appeared similar to English, there were many differences, and this sometimes caused a slight breakdown in communication, especially for the British teachers with stronger regional accents. I think I was doing okay but if I had been from Liverpool or Newcastle, it could have been interesting.

I was slowly adapting and life was becoming easier. After driving a few more miles, I came off at the next exit, turned back and drove home.

Back at my apartment, I lay on my bed feeling tired, yet reflective. I thought about that short and thought-provoking journey, the miles quickly clocking up, the feelings I had, the music I listened to, the words I heard, the fears that ran through my mind, the hopes I had and the anticipation of a new start.

The US 70 was a straight road that seemed to go on forever; I thought it would take me to places that I had never seen before and no doubt, would never see again. The average American spends approximately 101 minutes driving each day and I was sure, with all that time to myself, I would feel sad yet happy, lost yet found, lonely yet together, alone yet accompanied, anxious yet at peace, defeated yet hopeful about this new chapter.

My new American home, job, car and friends may not have lasted forever, but this part of my new journey in life was making me stronger, and whatever the obstacles, I knew I would get over them and find myself.

23

I ate my 'non-American breakfast', showered, dressed and left the apartment to enjoy my 'American weekend'. I walked out into the bright sunshine towards my car and slowly, yet excitedly, drove from my complex down Amelia Church Road.

Driving on the right now felt normal, although several days earlier, it felt surreal, as everything in the car and on the road felt opposite. The green and white overhead traffic signs still seemed strange, even more than the strange names written across them.

I then took a slip road on to the US 70 West, accelerating quickly to my normal cruising speed of sixty miles per hour, enjoying that deliberate and sudden surge of speed each time. Looking up at the signs, at junction 301, I drove on the slip road right to US 64 East / I-440 West, heading towards Raleigh and then at junction 7B, took another slip road right to US 70 West / NC 50 North towards the sign 'Crabtree Valley/Durham', driving past a McDonald's on the corner. I was tempted to stop there out of sheer curiosity but for the massive queue of pickup trucks at the drive thru – in fact, most of the cars around there were, indeed, monstrous pick-up trucks dwarfing my humble family saloon.

I then turned left, on to Blue Ridge Road and, lastly, turned right on to Crabtree Valley Avenue and arrived at the shopping mall.

My first impression was that the mall looked full of exclusive stores and was busy with weekend shoppers. I ambled around, generally looking and taking everything in my stride and then took the escalator up to the second floor packed full of boutiques, makeup shops and shoe shops, all positioned along narrow balconies.

Some clothing stores I had not seen before, including Banana Republic, seemed expensive but I liked their style of clothes – mainly khaki coloured shorts and stripy fashionable rugby shirts. A common dress code of North Carolinians was baggy shorts, sleeveless vests displaying many tattoos and flip- flops, which seemed appropriate

131

footwear in this climate.

I entered a furnishing store, browsed for a while and bought a lamp and several scatter cushions, to make my apartment look homely.

On the way back, I drove to Walmart to buy a TV cable so I could now blend into more 'American culture' by watching TV. That evening, I noticed many of the TV commercials had special effects, unlike our more basic adverts in the UK.

Later that same evening, I went out with the 'Viffers' to an Irish bar in downtown Raleigh (they are big on Irish pubs here!) and stupidly drank several pints of North Carolinian Pale Ale which tasted 'peculiar'. We were 'priming' ourselves for our first week at our schools, although I ended up getting drunk and spent half of Sunday in bed, vomiting several times during the night. I slowly recovered, staying in my PJs for most of the day and watching TV. Around 7 p.m., Ade knocked on the door and wanted to go out into Raleigh for a pizza. I think we were both feeling homesick and beer-sick! As we arrived in Raleigh, we managed to locate a bohemian pizzeria and ate pizza topped with sundried tomatoes, artichokes and olives – culture after all!

It was a foolish idea to get drunk, and I was in bed by 9 p.m. that evening. I was still feeling delicate and not really in the mood for starting at my new school in the morning, but luckily, it was a non-teaching week for all the Viffers – so there were five days of what they referred to as 'work days' –a gentle warm-up for the weeks ahead.

As the week passed, I slowly got used to everything and did a lot of planning, especially for math.

The drive to school each morning was relaxing and I enjoyed listening to music and just switching off as I marvelled at the beautiful rural scenery. I had to be in school quite early and by the end of the week, I seemed to be driving on autopilot most mornings, ignoring all the green and white over- hanging road signs.

I had also spent two days that week in other schools in Johnston County attending training courses on math and science and meeting other teachers. We had visited a high school on one course where one of the teachers looked like she was about to give birth at any moment, yet was still very casually dressed in T-shirt and jeans.

I had memorised my new landline number and zip code which contained lots of 'faaves' and was looking forward to receiving my first phone call.

24

It was my first day of teaching and, after leaving my apartment ridiculously early, I noticed how empty the highway was, especially as I drove around a winding curve of the I-95 and approached school at just after 7 a.m.

I walked from my car and entered the school and then arrived at my classroom. I stood at the doorway in a contemplative state of mind, and stared into the empty room, noticing its polished floors and the thirty desks arranged neatly in rows facing the white board – the janitors had added their finishing touch. Within the hour, it would be bustling with 8th graders, talking about their summer vacations, and I wondered what they would look and sound like. I placed my bag on the floor and carefully put my files on my empty desk. Although I had spent the last week familiarising myself with this room, today the school and the teachers seemed different – but then it was my first experience of a teaching day, as opposed to a 'work day', in North Carolina.

I walked to Hayley's room to find her quietly facing her desk, busily sending a text message – I waited before speaking.

'Good morning Hayley!'

She quickly looked round in surprise, greeting me with a huge smile as her eyes opened wide. 'Hey! Ahh yew ready?'

I smiled and grimaced. 'I just hope we understand each other.'

'Ahhm sure yew will be faane! Ahh yew okay with the math?'

'I've got the hang of the first chapter but I need to go through some more of the algebra with you sometime, if that's okay?'

'Yeah, of course.'

'I can't believe I'm about to teach American kids!'

'At least yew ha-y-ve th-y-at second block free, remember! Yew are so lucky, Ahh wish ahh had th-ay-t!' She quietly giggled and shook her head. 'Please, come and see me if yew need anythin'.'

Hayley was insistently reassuring, which I greatly appreciated. She was also effortlessly kind and I looked forward to working with her. I had a feeling we would get on well. She had the ability to make me laugh, even when nothing funny was said. She just had an air about her that made me see the hilarity of most situations, easing any anxieties and it helped me through my first few days of the unknown.

After our brief conversation, I walked into a half-full canteen of casually dressed kids; some boys and girls even wore silky football shirts, long baseball shorts and trainers but most wore jeans and T-shirts. This was refreshingly different to the uniformed schoolchildren in the UK that I had been used to teaching over the years and, at first, it felt odd. Casual dress was a privilege in British schools and was allowed only on 'mufti days' (when children did not have to wear uniforms) and usually, on the last day of the term.

I wondered what kind of a difference wearing a school uniform meant to a child. Attitudes to school uniforms vary from country to country and even from school to school within one country. I thought it was strange that British school children are often sent home or sometimes excluded for not wearing the correct uniform, or even receiving a detention for not wearing the correct length tie. Many people argue that even very young children learn valuable lessons from having to wear a school uniform, which will stand them in good stead in adult life. They learn to fit in, encouraging them to feel a sense of pride similar to when wearing the colours of their favourite football team. Some teachers even argue that students all wearing the same uniform combats bullying and irons out differences between richer and poorer, avoiding rich kids parading designer clothes in front of their less fortunate peers.

As I looked around the canteen, some kids were eating breakfast and others were talking and walking over to a small door at the back of the canteen, which connected to the 8th grade hall. I looked up at the oversized digital clock, positioned half way down on the breeze-block wall, displaying '7:27 a.m.' in bright red digits, before walking back to my room – time was fleeting.

I sat down at my desk and perused my lesson plans once again, which I had prepared meticulously, occasionally looking up around

135

the peaceful room. I suddenly stood up and walked over to one of the student's desks positioned near my desk.

'WOO!' I shouted with excitement and within minutes, the younger janitor quickly entered the room.

'Hey, are yew okay?'

'Yeah, I am just overexcited. Sorry to alarm you.'

'Ahh hope they didn't hear th-y-at, they maaght think yew are a li-dd-le crazy!'

'I've been a little crazy for a long time.'

'As long as you're okay? Aah w-y-ill leave yew to it then! Ha-y-ve a great day!'

'Thank you!'

Some students slowly walked into the room and looked at me strangely, as I sat at one of the student desks. They probably thought I was a very mature student or just plainly mad. Not only did they have casual attire but they had a casual approach, some of them walking half the speed I normally walk, even when I am not in a rush. They whispered to each other looking sheepish. I was not sure if they knew I was teaching them or maybe they thought I was an American teacher.

One boy wearing glasses confidently asked, 'Where dew we s-y-it?'

I stood up. 'Hold on, I have a class list and I am going to sit you in alphabetical order when you all arrive.'

He looked confused, giving me the impression he did not understand a single word. I decided to explain everything once the whole class had arrived. I went to the front of the room as it quickly filled with students and within a few minutes the classroom was quiet, despite being full of thirty wide-eyed students holding files and it was still early!

'Good morning! My name is Mr Wood.' I greeted them with a big smile, while looking around at them.

All the students stared at me with expressionless faces.

'I'd like to sit you in alphabetical order. Please could you all just stand at the side, I will call your name, point at a desk and if you can sit there please, that would be great. I will leave a seating plan on the notice board, just in case you forget.' I looked up smiling and started reading through the list of names, pointing to the desks where I wanted them to sit.

Some names sounded typically American: 'Candice, Tyler, Madison, Mary, Logan, Breanna, Nathan…Joseph.' I paused; 'What?' I quietly uttered, as I scanned the list and re-read the names 'Mary and Joseph?'

After calling out two 'Brandons' on the list, I stared at the next name and looked at their faces, then back at the names in disbelief as I nervously chewed my pen. I stared again at the group of standing students and then back at the name: Jesus, which seemed to stand out in the list.

'No way', I uttered and laughed nervously.

Before cautiously trying to pronounce it, I did not want to offend him or be the laughing stock of the entire class, the entire school or end up being headlines in the local press: 'British man meets Jesus in North Carolina!'

'*He-sus*?' I said warily, as a small Mexican boy suddenly moved forward, in response, holding a stack of files bigger than himself and I silently pointed to the desk where Jesus was going to be sitting. I looked at him briefly before quickly carrying on calling out their names and directing students to their seats until they were all seated. I looked across at the whole class, the majority of whom were white Americans.

I glanced at the list of names one more time concentrating on 'Mary, Joseph and Jesus'. I really wanted to laugh at the fact I had the equivalent of the Holy Family in my classroom and felt I should be asking, 'Moses … God … are you here, too?' I looked down at my desk, smiled and couldn't wait to send an email home – who would believe me!

'Okay guys, this is my seating plan, so if you can stay in these positions, I would really appreciate it.' I heard background laughter from my newly acquainted American audience.

'Sir, where are yew from?' one boy curiously asked.

'I am from England.'

'We are being taught by an inglish m-a-yn', another boy shouted out, generating cackles across the large classroom. His southern drawl sounded dreamlike.

There were more chuckles from my captive audience and I started giggling and could not stop. I think it was just nervousness or the way he said it, his timing, their surprised reactions, their accents, that place, the Holy Family and the whole experience all combined into one, and I whispered, 'this can't be happening to me.' My intermittent chuckles did not stop there, and I think my American spectators thought I had lost my mind. I just hoped they did not think I was making fun of them.

I had a pile of science textbooks stacked to the ceiling at the back of the room on the big high desk and each textbook weighed a ton. I walked over to them carrying my planner and pen.

'Okay! I am now going to give you a science textbook, so when I say your name, can you come up and collect one and when you return to your desk, can you please write your name at the front of the book on the white slip inside.'

One by one, I asked each student to come up and collect a book from the back desk. I recorded their book numbers, including Jesus' name: that was the closest I had ever been to a Jesus and I felt like making the sign of the cross over my chest. I really wanted to start chuckling but I had to force myself to stop.

I inhaled and exhaled forcefully, before introducing myself.

'Good morning. I am Mr Wood. I probably sound a bit strange compared to what you are used to hearing around school. I am from England and I am your new teacher of science and maths ... I mean math ... I will be teaching you science, first block and math, third block. As you have been in this school for two years already, you know the routines, so it's going to take a little time getting used to everything and I might need to ask you questions, at least for a while.' Expressionless faces continued to look at me as silence filled the room.

'Okay, why don't we start by breaking down some barriers here? I would like to talk to you about my background and I would also like to know a bit more about each and every one of you. I know you have your own paper, so can you get your pens out and write down something about yourself, where you live, your family, your favourite animal and all those kind-of-things.'

'Mr Woo-ood, what is a pin?' a pupil asked.

'Sorry?' I stopped in my tracks.

'What is a … pin?' he asked again curiously.

'Do you not know what a pen is?' I had a look of confusion on my face as they all continued to stare at me and some looked baffled with their mouths open or had glazed expressions.

'You said pin?' This still sounded like 'peeeeyn'.

'Ah!' I realised the misunderstanding, as I had forgotten how much vowels can be drawn out and as a result, 'pen' sounded very different. I walked over to my desk, picked up a pen (a biro) and held it up high for everyone to see. I also noticed Hayley stood at the back of the room who covered her mouth and started giggling discreetly.

'MR WOOD MEANS PE-Y-EN!' Hayley shouted but she looked amused. They all looked around at her – a familiar face.

'Yes. P-y-en!' I tried to imitate Hayley. 'Thanks Miss Penrose.' I did a thumbs up at her.

'Yew give Mr Wood an easy taame, okay!' She smiled and walked away, looking back at me as we exchanged smiles.

'But we don't wraate in pe-y-en, we use pe-y-nsil.'

'Really?' I was not sure what I was more worried about: the fact that they wrote in pencil or the fact they did not understand me saying the word. I had a feeling that I was going to get lost in translation.

'I am glad we have got that sorted!'

An African American boy then asked me a question. 'What's yer fa-vor-rat aanimal, Mr Woo-ood?'

'A grey wolf.' I walked over to the whiteboard and wrote on it in big capital letters: **GREY WOLF**.

'Yew don't sp'yell it laake th-a-yt Mr Woo-ood', he added. This quickly generated into what seemed like canned laughter across the entire classroom.

'We do in England. Come up to the board and show me how you spell it then. I'm curious.'

As he walked slowly, I noticed he wore an oversized white and blue silky matching baseball shirt and shiny long baseball shorts. I also noticed the way he was walking: every time he took a step, he seemed to limp with one leg while at the same time dipping with the same shoulder, like a strut. I think someone once said it was a called a 'pimp limp'.

As he approached the board, I imagined what boys would be wearing in a top private school in London: probably a suit and walking as quickly as possible to the board to avoid being told off his teacher. I handed him a marker pen and he scrawled the American alternative across the whiteboard in large untidy writing: **GRAY WOLF**.

'Ah, that is how you spell it here.'

'Yup', he replied and proudly smiled back at 'his' captive audience, strutted back to his desk high- fiving some of his friends on the way as if it was some major achievement. Maybe it was – for him.

We spent the next fifteen minutes or so translating. I wrote a table of words on the board and they told me how to spell them in American.

English	American
colour	color
favourite	favorite
foetus	fetus
apologise	apologize
tyre	tire
fibre	fiber

The conversation of how to pronounce words continued and they all seemed fascinated by it, as was I. When I said 'aluminium', they instantly burst into fits of laughter and then had the audacity to correct me with 'al-um-min-um', and they pronounced 'route' as 'rowte'. I also told them we have roundabouts, which puzzled them but after further explanation, they told me they call them 'circles'.

'Okay. I'll tell you what. Why don't you all put your pencils down and come to the front of the room, please.' Suddenly they all stood up and each one looked deep in thought.

I quickly glanced at the clock, suddenly realising they were going to say the Pledge! I moved to the side of the room, as every student placed their hands over their chests – I presumed over their hearts – and spoke in unison, in southern drawl, in time with the principal who's softly

140

spoken voice was just about audible through the tannoy system. A strange stillness filled the room before they spoke.

'Aah ple-dge allegiance to the fl-yag of the Uni-ded States of America, and to the republic for which it st-a-ynds, one nation under God, indivisible, with liber-dy and justice for aall.'

The inauguration of the pledge or oath happened in 1892, on the 400th anniversary of the discovery of America, also known as Columbus Day. The Pledge of Allegiance words are a national symbol of America and Congress did not officially recognise these words until the 22 June, 1942, when they were formally included in the US Flag Code.

I still could not imagine British kids doing this, without some form of rebellion as they ignorantly talk about which computer games they play or throw things at each other. They should encourage more 'Britishness' in schools in the UK, in just the same way as they are continually promoting nationalism in America.

I stood and observed and respected their patriotic routine and tried not to think of this negatively, although it could be seen as indoctrination. These children would go through this routine at the same time on each school morning, starting from the moment they could walk and talk and lasting for the whole of their school life, and it was to become part of my morning routine.

Following the pledge, they silently remained standing, looking at me, waiting for further instructions and I suddenly remembered I asked them to stand before the pledge – I appreciated their manners.

'Please, all come to the front and sit on the floor while I talk to you.'

They all gathered around the front glass cabinet where I had set up a small exhibition of photographs, text and objects. These included images of London, facts about England, postcards of places I had visited and the royal family, and tacky souvenirs: a red telephone box, a black cab and a silver mini with a Union Jack on its roof. I also included a greater display of photographs of some European capitals I had visited, as well as the pyramids in Egypt.

141

Another important part of my job, and part of my official job title, was to be a cultural ambassador for VIF; there was an expectation I would exchange information about my culture. I wanted to get to know my students and just hoped they were as equally curious about me as I was of them. I had a feeling that many of them had never met anyone British before and I had also never met American kids – it was a new experience for all of us.

'Is there anything you want to ask?'

There was complete silence, again. They looked shy but had excitement in their eyes. 'Surely, there must be something?' One boy raised his hand.

'Is brid-en a country?'

'I'm sorry. What is your name again?'

'Nathan.'

'Nathan, that's it. It is going to take me time to get used to all of your names. Great Britain is made up of three countries: England, Wales and Scotland. The United Kingdom includes these three countries and Northern Ireland. We call it either Great Britain, Britain or the United Kingdom, or most people call it the UK.'

Nathan smiled. 'Yew speak f-y-ast.'

'Do I?' I attempted to slow down.

'Can I ask you another question?' he asked.

'Sure.'

'Dew yew laak it here?' he asked, genuinely.

'Do you mean North Carolina or America?'

'North Carol-aana.'

'Oh … right. I like it here. The people are friendly and I like the countryside, and the weather is much better here.'

'We heard it rains allot in ingland', one small girl said.

'You're right. It does rain a lot but we get a little bit of sunshine too.' Okay, it's your turn. Nathan, tell me something about North Carolina.'

'We ha-y-ve football teams here.'

'You call it soccer, right?'

'No!' Many of them laughed in response.

'Sorry, I'm pretty useless. You will have to educate me. All I know is, your football is called American football, which reminds me of English rugby, although I don't know the rules of American football, and you call football 'soccer', is that right?'

'Yeah, that's raaght!'

'We don't have soccer teams here.'

'Oh right! So, tell me about soccer then?'

'We don't have b-i-y-g teams here like yew h-a-yve in Great Brid-en. Which soccer team do yew laake, Sir?'

'Well, we call football soccer also, but soccer is like a slang word. Do you know what I mean? It is just like a nickname, but we have big football teams or soccer teams in England. The team that I support is Liverpool. Have you heard of that place? You might have heard of the Beatles. They also came from Liverpool.'

I suddenly broke into song. 'We all live in a yellow submarine...a yellow submarine. I stopped singing quicker than I started. 'Have you heard of that song?'

They all stared at me.

'I guess you haven't. Well, that is a famous song by the Beatles. Maybe we should all sing it one day. I'm joking!' I was not sure if they were laughing at my singing or me.

'Yes. I ha-y-ve heard of the-y-m', a small Mexican girl quietly said. She then asked, 'Yew ha-y-ve a team called Manchester Uni-ded, right?'

'Yes, we do. Have you all heard of them?'

Many of them nodded slowly and looked at each other. At last, I sparked some interest. 'You might have heard of ... David Beckham?'

'Y-eah, we ha-y-ve. He is married to Victoria Beckham.'

'Is she in a pop group?' another girl asked. The whole class seemed to come alive at this point.

'Yes, she was in a pop group called the Spice Girls. You might have heard of them?' Many of them nodded. Even in the backwaters of North Carolina, they had heard of the Spice Girls.

'So please tell me about the American football teams here in North Carolina. We kind of got side- tracked.'

'Saade-tra-y-cked, wh-y-at does th-a-yt mean?'

'It means when you start talking about other things.' I tried to

143

explain the best way I could.

We continued talking about American football for some time and not really about each other's countries. I found out that North Carolina is home to the Carolina Panthers who play their home games at a big seater stadium in Charlotte. Nathan knew everything about them and gave me a ten minute running commentary on the Panthers: 'They play-y-ed their first season in naanty-naanty-faave at the Memorial Stadium in South Carol-aana. In February tew-thous-y-and fore, the P-ay-nthers play-ed in Super Bowl thirdy-ate and in too-thous-a-y-and, the P-ay-nthers play in Sooper Bowl fifty.'

I stared at him before answering. 'You know a lot about them, Nathan, but, thank you for educating me!'

'You h-ay-ve a royal family too? Is Philip the King?' another student asked.

'No, he is not, but I know why you might think that. Prince Philip is married to the Queen.'

'If he is married to a queen, should he be a ki-y-ng?'

'It's quite hard to explain but for a man to become a king, he has to be born as a royal person. Philip married the Queen, and he was not originally royal, so he became a prince and cannot become a king. I don't fully understand how it all works, but if a woman marries a future king, then she will become a queen. I know, it all sounds confusing.'

'What is the food laake in ingland? Do you have gri-y-ts?'

'What are gri-y-ts?' I asked inquisitively, exaggerating the word as she did.

Some of the class laughed and then, another boy answered me. 'It's made from corn and tastes laake porridge. It tastes good with bacon.' He then smiled and looked proud after delivering his recommendation. 'You should traa it!'

'I will. We have something called fish and chips, which is fish fried in batter (I pronounced it as 'bad-der') and it is served with fries. That tastes good and I miss it too.' I suddenly thought about my local fish and chip shop in my hometown of Rochdale making me quickly smile.

The conversation continued focusing on culture and listening to the students; I forgot about actually teaching them. We talked more about the differences between English and American football, food, music, weather and the royal family. I had not appreciated how sport is such a big part of American life and this starts from an early age.

I think the students understood some things that I had talked about: the capital cities in the UK and they knew England had many professional football teams (especially the boys). It seemed Manchester United is quite well known there, due to David Beckham and the Spice Girls although they had not heard of other British pop groups and only one girl had heard of the Beatles but maybe that was a generational thing.

I had also learnt North Carolina had only one football team called Tar Heels, represented by the symbol of N and C intertwined (sometimes with a ram in the middle of it). I also talked about black taxi-cabs in London and red telephone boxes and they told me only 'poor people' walk.

Also, North Carolina has a state flag (as do all American states) which is blue, red and white; the state bird is the Northern Cardinal; and the state's nicknames are 'The Old North State' and 'The Tar Heel State'. 'Tar Heel' is a nickname applied both to the state and its inhabitants. It is also the nickname of the University of North Carolina's athletic teams and their fans, and the students. I was curious as to why it is called 'Tar Heel' – I presumed something to do with tar on shoes?

We compared the weather; they had the impression it rains constantly in England (sometimes it feels that way) and they told me hurricanes are common. Sometimes there can be twenty every year. I always complain when it is wet and windy in England – from now on I won't! They also asked me if it snowed in England (I paused and said sometimes, but more when I was child). They told me it snows heavily in the winter and they usually get 'two or three snow days' (an expression I had not heard of before, meaning they don't come in to school on those days) and they seemed happy about that – who wouldn't be?

I was impressed as they told me that Charlotte was the most populated city, even though Raleigh is the state capital. On a personal level, it appeared that the majority of students were from Kenley and some lived in trailers.

I had certainly been educated and knew a lot more about them and North Carolina than when I first entered the room an hour before. This had been a good exchange of cultures and I hoped to do more sessions.

Suddenly, *Channel 1 News* came on the TV – just as scheduled, at 9.25 a.m. They all quickly changed positions on the floor and stared at the small TV screen fixed to the wall for ten minutes. It was only American news and it seemed odd there was no mention of the UK, the weather, the royal family or anything else that I was used to seeing back home. The words 'America at War' flashed across the screen several times during the news slot in large, bright yellow font. All these students from a young age seemed bombarded with this, thinking America was at war with Libya.

It had been an interesting first day but it was time to go home. Despite feeling tired, I decided to take a detour to Smithfield Library instead and sent my next email.

15 August, 2003

I cannot believe I have been here for four weeks! American culture has finally hit home and strangely, I'm settling into my life and routine, even though I still have hurdles to get over, as I need to drive all the way to Charlotte to get my visa verified due to a processing error by the American Embassy back in London. If I do not get this dealt with, I may be 'booted' out of this country and America does not mess around. I am not looking forward to the 500-mile round trip, and I have to get there by 7.30 am. The next hurdle is to get my speeding ticket sorted out for driving over the speed limit on my first long journey. If it is not one thing, it is something else. My car had the wrong licence plate, so I have to get that sorted. Licence plates only have three letters, a dash and four numbers on them and they only have a rear license plate here too. Most licence plates in NC have a slogan 'First in Flight' with a silhouette of the Wright Brothers' plane – representing the birth of aviation. If I had a South Carolina plate fitted to my car, I would be in jail – not sure if I would look good in an orange boiler suit. I was also doing reading up on North Carolina; it is one of the original 13 colonies and it is the 9th most popular state of the 50 United States.

I've a court appearance to attend on the 27 of August. The teachers at my school advised me to get a DA (district attorney), which I am in the process of doing, they go to court for you and you normally pay them $350 or so. This has happened to some other teachers in my school but created a few laughs in the staffroom and the rumour quickly spread around the school. It is very tempting to press the pedal to the metal when you are driving a two-litre car on the big open highways that seem wide enough to drive one of those of Wright Brothers' aeroplanes on.

Teaching here is certainly an experience. I still cannot get my head around the fact that the kids have to say the Pledge every morning. The principal's voice comes through a speaker system, although he still sounds quiet. When this happens, they all suddenly stand up, like clockwork, face the American flag and start speaking their allegiance. It reminds me of a scene out of the Stepford Wives. Each teaching period or 'block' lasts 90 mins, which is quite a long time to keep kids entertained and they all call me Mr Woo'oood. It seems Wood is more drawn out every day – I am sure they are doing it on purpose. I have been 'advised' to pace my lessons with a wide range of engaging activities. But get this, the kids all work in complete silence (I think they are still trying to suss me out or maybe it is still the honeymoon period). They all watch the news on Channel 1 at 9.25 a.m. for 10 mins each morning. Today, the news bulletin was about Libya. At my school, we have to create a web page so we can load our homework onto it for students and parents to access. It is rather basic with some simple animations of dancing pencils, and can only be accessed by the school zip code. I like it but it is extra work each day keeping it updated.

I'll write more soon.

Lader...Px

25

As I drove to school, I thought about the endearing remark, 'Is Philip the King?', which made me chuckle. I already liked the kids and I also liked the drive each morning, as I always arrived feeling relaxed.

Considering it was rush hour, the traffic flowed well, assisted by the sheer amount of space, wide motorways and a much smaller population. In fact, North Carolina had a population of around 10 million compared to the 50 million people in England and both are of similar size. On some mornings, it was similar to driving on the M6 on Christmas Day. There seemed to be no road works, and if there were, men worked tirelessly throughout the night under floodlights, no matter what weather conditions, unlike in England, were you see one man at the side of the motorway holding a brush while puffing on a cigarette or waiting until the drizzle has stopped.

At school, I took my third block to lunch. This was the same class I taught science too, but now they were doing maths. They only had thirty minutes to eat, so I went with them to collect my food, served again on a white compartmentalised tray. This time I chose mashed potatoes, chicken nuggets and barbeque sauce, peas, a cookie and fruit inside a clear plastic container swishing around in what I could only describe as syrup – all rinsed down with electric blue Gatorade. Most of the kids ate and drank this daily, as did some teachers and there did not appear to be much choice, although there was pizza on the menu for the following day!

I sat down at the teachers' table, opposite a hall full of students. It was noisy and everyone was chatting, including the teachers. For the first time, I noticed that there were many overweight kids and all of them seemed to use piles of napkins as they ate. Each time they put a fork full of food into their mouths, they wiped their lips immediately and delicately afterwards, repeating this at least thirty times until they finished eating – I admired their finesse.

For the first time, I sat opposite the two teachers who were married. 'Hey, how's it goin' Pauuul?' Mr Barton asked.

'Okay, so far, thank you!'

'I am Spencer Barton and th-i-ys is my waafe, Liz Barton.' I had noticed Americans introduced themselves with both names.

'Pleased to meet yew, Pauuul', she politely said.

'Pleased to meet you both.' I looked at them while eating and a garden pea fell out of my mouth and rolled slowly and directly towards her plate as they both watched.

'I think my pea is happy to meet you too!' I blushed as they both giggled and I picked up the pea quickly. She seemed friendly, although the husband seemed inquisitive, asking me where in England I was from and how British schools compared to American schools. This conversation lasted all through my lunch break while I tried to avoid letting any more garden peas escape.

Spencer stopped eating and then looked at me, for several seconds, looking serious, and asked in strong southern drawl, 'Do y'all have trees in ingland?'

I nearly choked on my electric blue, sickly sweet Gatorade.

'Sorry, you caught me off guard.' I continued coughing as everyone around me laughed and after composing myself, I replied, 'Yeah, of course we do! Why do you ask?'

As his wife ate, she quietly giggled and rolled her eyes in embarrassment while shaking her head, as if she expected him to say that. He was persistent and continued with his line of questioning.

'I've seen phodo-gra-y-fs of the Brid-ish country-saade in a b-oook and they don't ha-y-ve trees.'

'Can you remember which part of Britain it was?'

'I think it was some place called … moors?' I continued to look at him puzzled.

'Ah, you mean the Yorkshire Moors?'

'Y'es! Aah was readin' about the Yorkshire Moors. Is tha-y-t how yew say it?'

I wanted to laugh, as he overemphasised his r's.

'The moors are open grasslands so there aren't usually any trees there. We do have trees, of course, as most countries do, but they are usually in woods or forested areas, although they grow anywhere really.' My hometown is near some moors called the Pennines and there are no trees their either. Maybe that is why you think there are no trees in England?'

I felt like showing him my own photographs of the open savannah in South Africa I had visited, just to wipe the silly smirk of his face.

'Moors, moors, moors?' He tried to say the word several times in a more anglicised accent each time and then shook his head. 'That's an unusual word.' Before he started eating, he looked perplexed for some time! 'We just call em' plains here.'

'As in the plains of North Carolina?' I asked.

'Aah reckon.'

'I also noticed you have many conifers here'.

'Sorry, say th-a-yt ag-a-yn?' He looked at me, puzzled.

'I noticed you have lots of conifers here', I said again.

'Yew mean, fir trees?'

'Yeah, fir trees. We have more deciduous trees in our woodlands and forests.'

'We ha-y-ve deciduous trees too.' This seemed to be turning into some weird kind of the US versus the UK nature contest.

His questions about trees reminded me of a time when I was looking out of the windows of the crown inside the Statue of Liberty several years ago. I was talking to my friend from university who I was travelling with and a woman from Texas overheard me. After the usual, 'Are you from England?' routine, she then went on to ask me: 'Do you have microwaves in England?' I thought that sounded as equally absurd as the trees question. Americans must think we still live in the Victorian times.

Apart from pertinent questioning, the teachers were nice but they must have thought I was a charity case, or else they were just extremely generous: yesterday all the 8th grade teachers unexpectedly arrived at my math lesson to give me a 'shower'. I had heard of baby showers before but not an 'apartment shower'. They really helped me out, even the dead man's shirts came in handy! This had never happened in any English school! They gave me towels, a new iron and silverware. Maybe they thought English people eat with their hands!

After lunch, I went back to my classroom, sat at my desk and looked through my lesson notes for my last block. I was so focused on reading, I didn't notice anyone walk in.

'Hey, Mr Woo-ood. Aa'm Shakila.' Before I could answer her, she had both hands on the desk and everything spilled out from her extremely low cleavage. My natural reaction should have been to avert my eyes, but I felt surrounded by Shakila and almost every part of her oversized anatomy.

I suddenly and clumsily stood up, moving backwards pushing into the chair, which dragged on the polished floor making another screech.

'Hi Shakila!' I guardedly responded, as I moved backwards. Suddenly, the janitor rushed in.

'Wh-a-yt have ahh told yew about scratchin' up this floor, Mr Woo-ood!' She winked and walked out as quickly as she walked in, looking back smiling.

'Erm, Shakila, I have got some work to do. I will see you in the block later, okay!'

'Okay, Mr Woo-ood.'

I sighed and sat down.

It was the end of the week. Teachers from 6th grade invited me to a hog roast at the weekend and asked me to go with them to the local abattoir to collect the hog, watch them prepare it by cutting it in half, and then spit roast it, but I politely declined the offer.

A former work colleague from England had emailed me, telling me Venus flytraps are native to North and South Carolina. I was interested in seeing some and maybe I could feed them the giant spiders that lived in the forest that I had driven past – I knew they lived there as I had pulled over, got out of my car and noticed huge webs, straight out of a scene from the *Hobbit*. I had quickly driven off shuddering, as I did not fancy being lunch for some man-eating spider.

As I drove home, I thought about exploring Raleigh that weekend. But it rained heavily, so hard in fact, that most of the cars had to pull over, including myself – it looked like scene from a science-fiction movie! It seemed there had been massive thunderstorms and an electrical storm wiping out the power in New York and even parts of Canada.

Despite being in North Carolina for a just few weeks, I was managing well on my own and was quickly adapting to American life.

26

Today, I had a good excuse for not going into school: I needed to verify my visa but I had to drive all the way to Charlotte to do this. I first had to seek permission from the principal, of course, who subtly smirked when I told him my reason but he allowed me to go.

I left my apartment, just after midnight, arriving in Charlotte at an unearthly hour. After eventually finding it even though I had printed off the directions, I eventually parked next to the compact-sized immigration office building in the empty car park. I pressed the door-lock switch and adjusted my seat into a more comfortable position, in order to have a quick sleep before sunrise, following my three-hour early morning drive.

I slowly opened my eyes one last time to look at the building, only to find myself staring into a man's face pressed against my driver's window.

'AHHHGGH!'

The man started knocking hard on the window and shone a bright flash torch into my face as my eyes squinted.

'WHAT DO YOU WANT?' I banged my head on the roof of the car, fully awake within a nanosecond as he tried to open the locked door.

'WHAT ARE YOU DOING?' He shouted.

'DON'T HURT ME!'

'I'M SECUR-IDY!'

I stared at him for several seconds, still in a state of shock and disbelief despite him wearing a uniform and cap, before pressing the button for the electric window to open a crack.

'What did I do wrong?' My voice resonated in the deadly quietness – even the crickets stopped chirping!

'Nothing Sir!'

I opened the window fully. 'You gave me a fright!'

'Aam sorry sir.'

'I thought you were gonna…never mind.'

He started laughing, deeply. Had the world gone completely mad?

He was African American, in his sixties and as he continued laughing, I gradually composed myself. 'Yew need to start ged-ding in laane at about four thir-dy as people start arriving about faave' His accent was also drawled and 'five', sounded like 'faaaaaaaaaaaave'! 'Have a good day, Sir!'

The larger-than-life security guard smiled, raised his cap and walked away – extremely slowly as my heart still raced. I looked at him again as he disappeared slowly into the darkness. I was certain a newly born joey would have crawled faster into its mother's pouch.

I was three hundred miles further south, but the accent was more or less the same. Accents in the UK change drastically between relatively close cities, for instance Manchester and Liverpool, a distance of about 35 miles. I slouched back into my seat and spoke aloud: 'What the hell am I doing here?' I looked at my watch and it was 4 am. I took his advice, locked the car behind me and walked towards the building.

It was humid already, even at this time. I was first in line and sat down on the dusty doorstep opposite the entrance. People started to arrive within thirty minutes and I checked my watch again – he was spot-on with his timing! The first to arrive looked mainly Mexican and El Salvadoran. I leant my head against the wall to try to get some sleep. This could be a long day!

I was woken up by the loudest and strangest scream from a toddler and was certain he was auditioning for a Stephen King movie. I thought it would be in my best interests to stay awake until the office opened. People arrived in droves and it was unbelievable how quickly so many people accumulated near the office.

Finally, 8.30 a.m. arrived and the door swiftly opened. I walked to the desk and was greeted by a smiling woman, wearing more make-up than a model in a Max Factor commercial.

'Hey! Have you come far?'

'From Clayton, near Raleigh', I replied.

'Not th-a-yt far th-y-en.'

She stamped some documents and within one minute, she said.

'You're done!'

'At least, I won't have to go back to the UK now!' She did not understand me, so I calmly walked away.

'Yew enjoy yer stay, Sir. Have a go-od day.' I looked back, smiled and nodded.

After all that time worrying, the long drive, nearly suffering a cardiac arrest in the car park and sitting on a doorstep for the best part of four hours with half the population of South America around me, my situation was resolved eight and a half hours later in just sixty seconds – but at least I had a valid visa!

I decided to go for breakfast – no, not at Tiffany's, but a fast food chain called Bojangles' famous for its chicken and biscuits.

I had chicken with grits and sausage. The grits had a strange porridge-like texture but I quite liked it and now I could tell the kids I had tried some. I had lemon tea and a biscuit (which was in fact, a scone) and then asked an old man who looked ninety years old for the directions back to Raleigh. I somewhat already knew the way but really wanted some conversation with someone local.

After literally telling me his life story, he gave me the directions. This was after he had told me that he had fought in Vietnam. He pronounced it 'Nom'. His story was interesting but seemed stereotypical, as if I had heard it before. However, I listened to what he had to say, despite feeling exhausted. Then, he started to tell me what Charlotte was like in the 1950s and how the speed limit used to be twenty miles per hour on most roads around town.

He was fascinated that I was from the UK and asked many questions about the Second World War, the royal family and London. He made me feel that what I had to say was interesting and the things that I had taken for granted in my daily life really engaged his curiosity.

It was then time to drive back, although I had been putting it off as I was enjoying his interesting stories, so I politely made my excuses to leave.

Overall it had been a productive day, with a few more hurdles cleared. I had also sorted out my speeding ticket but I had to pay for

155

a DA costing me $400. At least I would not have to appear in court. I decided to make a detour around the area before driving back. Many of the houses had shutters and were painted in pale colours – they looked like they were built in the 1930s. There were also many exotic trees and that gave the area a tropical feel, just like the man who once described it when I was in Italy.

I arrived back in Clayton late afternoon, having witnessed my first, fairly bad, traffic jam on the US 70. There was not much in Clayton but a post office, a fire station, three shops and a coffee shop. I decided to walk to the post office to post my letter to the DA and to get some exercise. I thought it wouldn't take long, but I had little understanding of how far it was to walk around a block. In fact, I ended up walking half a mile and had to cross some train tracks. I will never use the expression 'around the block again'.

I stopped to watch the train move slowly over the level crossing. I had seen model trains move faster! I think Americans take health and safety just a little too seriously. In England, trains whizz through crossings and it is no wonder cars are smashed up and people are killed! It was the same with ambulances and fire engines: they looked old and also moved slowly, with three times as many sirens blaring out and lights flashing.

The post office was the size of Buckingham Palace, with virtually no customers and just a few staff; in fact, it felt slightly eerie.

It started to rain and I became soaked walking back to my car but at least everything was finally organised and now I did not have to worry about being deported!

27

Late September 2003

A lot had happened in a relatively short time, but living in North Carolina felt refreshingly 'normal'. Driving a car on the opposite side of the road now seemed automatic and southern drawl did not sound like southern drawl anymore, in fact, communication both ways seemed easier and I was enjoying living there. After buying a computer and being online enabled easier communication with the outside world, although I would miss Gunshot Grannie – maybe I would visit her once in a while and listen to her stories.

Teaching was in full swing and all I did was eat, sleep and grade papers. Last week was 'grading week' and I ended up working three 12-hour days, knocking ten years off my life span – teaching can be a solitary life! I think the teaching profession should come with a health warning, or even better, a 'don't-do-it' warning.

Teachers do seem to work harder in the US but earn considerably less than their European colleagues. The role of an American teacher includes being a facilitator, a psychologist, a counsellor, a passive listener, a parent, a role model, an advisor, a friend, a minder, a lunchtime supervisor, a mediator and an actual teacher!

Sadly, in the US, if a teacher moves to certain states, usually they have to start at the bottom of the pay-scale again, which seems grossly unfair. This is unlike England, where teachers can earn the same, or more (especially in the private sector), wherever they work. Teachers living in the London boroughs receive extra pay, although it does not really compensate for the higher cost of living and accommodation in or around the capital. Outside of London and some of the fringe counties, teachers in the state sector earn the same, whether they live in the poorest or the wealthiest of areas.

Over the last few days there had been a lot of news coverage of Hurricane Isobel, which was due to hit the East Coast anywhere between New Jersey and North Carolina, with wind speeds expected to reach 106 miles per hour, just beyond comprehension.

We had practiced a hurricane drill at school the day before, which involved everyone having to sit on the floor in the corridor, just in case she struck. We were told that Isobel could be devastating – that was going to be one big hurdle! We would be told more details at school the next day but it was quite likely that school would be closed for two or three days, or possibly longer, as a precaution and if there was widespread damage.

The hurricane that hit NC in 1996 was not as bad as the predictions for Isobel, yet schools in Johnston County closed down for ten days. The schools there also act as refugee centres.

We had been given a list of things to buy: water, tinned food, baby food (which is highly nutritious and does not require cooking), candles and sleeping bags – just in case! Power lines and telephones might also go down so all contact with home would cease! This was on the news 24/7 and it was overkill!

Thinking about work, I had realised, it does not really matter where you live, life is really the same. It just happens to be a different place with different people. However, I was still enjoying 'American life'.

There was no school that Friday; well the kids were out but the teachers were in. Teaching would be a much more pleasant experience if we did not have to teach! I took part in four workshops which were all technology based and I used a computer package called 'time-liners' to create my own timeline of my life, which was interesting. I realised the more eventful episodes that happened were: buying my flat in London, going into a heart hospital when I was diagnosed with a heart murmur, being in relationships with Phil and Nick and moving to the States, yet there was a huge chunk of my life that looked worryingly empty; of course, I missed out the break up from last year (as obviously that was not exciting!).

After attending several interesting workshops, I went to the mall with Tee. We drove across the parking lot (she still thought walking was 'weird'). I spent over $100 on new clothing and then we treated ourselves to a nice dinner at an Italian restaurant that served humungous portions of delicious food – they really wanted you to instantly add those extra inches to your waistline.

It was the first decent meal I had eaten in some time. However, I had become addicted to Arby's and could not resist driving past it each time, but without ordering my 'usual meal': a roast beef and melted cheese sandwich, curly, spicy fries and Mountain Dew – I blame my addiction on Tee. Even driving back from the Italian restaurant, I was tempted to call in to Arby's again for yet another, 'quick fix'.

I had also become partial to sweet tea: ice cubes in cold tea or cold tea with crushed ice, lemon and ten tons of sugar. I thought I would surely be returning to the UK with Type 2 diabetes or, worse, inside a body bag! However, all of this sugar prompted me to join a local 24/7 gym, called Planet Fitness: in order to delay morbid obesity setting in. It had a bargain monthly fee and my free induction was the following day.

I did feel sluggish and I felt as though I had gained half my body weight since arriving two months ago. Maybe I was destined to become a barrel? I thought I should grade the student papers while on a treadmill or by the open-air pool, but my expanding stomach would have got in the way.

Although school was tiring, it was time to become healthier; go to the gym regularly and eat better food, although it would have been easier just to get in the car and go to drive-thru fast-food restaurants without having to get out of my car at all.

I had also decided to travel more at the weekends and see more of this state. Fellow Viffers and American work colleagues told me that Charleston in South Carolina is a nice place to visit, with something interesting around every corner in the historic district, and there is great nightlife and incredible food, rich art, culture, personality and southern charm that is difficult to beat.

After my recent visit, I knew it was a four-hour drive but that seemed like nothing. I quite liked the idea of just stepping out of my apartment and being transported to yet another place, even though I was doing the driving. I liked being alone cocooned in my car, listening to music and zoning out, yet feeling safe. Driving seemed like a relaxing past-time and I wondered about asking Tee if she wanted to come with me the following weekend. Tee agreed, and then casually invited me to her parents' house at Thanksgiving and possibly, a trip to New York and Niagara Falls. I also wanted to ask Ade but he had started dating a Mexican woman and, sadly, of late, I did not see much of him – maybe he had eloped to Mexico!

During that week, Hayley asked Tee and me to visit Blue Ridge Parkway at the weekend. As we had nothing planned, we decided to go and to my surprise, Ade, surprisingly appeared and came to my apartment on Friday afternoon and agreed to come with us, which I was happy about.

On Saturday morning, Tee came over to meet me and Ade at my apartment, and shortly after, Hayley arrived in her SUV who drove us all to the Blue Ridge Parkway. Most of the journey was on the I-40 and we saw road-kill the entire route: dogs, deer, racoons and anything else that had four legs - I thought I was witnessing the start of the next mass extinction.

'There are more dead deer than living ones', Ade joked.

'I know! Imagine, hi-dd-ing one of those? My car would end up as road ki-yll!' Hayley quipped. She should have gone into stand-up comedy, not teaching.

'Can you imagine hitting a moose?' Tee added.

'There would be nothing of us left', Ade quipped. 'I think I'd prefer to see a living moose.' Ade had a sympathetic view when it came to animals.

'There are supposed to be armadillos here too', I piped up.

'How random!' said Tee.

We arrived around four hours later. There was a chill in the air. Ade and I wore shorts and hoodies, while Tee and Hayley dressed sensibly in jeans and hoodies.

Once we had parked up, we asked a stranger to take a photograph of the four of us at a viewing point on the ridgeway. After having several photographs taken, I looked back at the view.

'It's really beaud-iful Hayley', commented Tee.

I had read the book *Into the Woods* by Bill Bryson and still remembered some of the scenes he describes: visions of forests and blue misty mountains.

'We will be lucky to see bears, as I thi-y-nk they are further up in the mountains, but yew never know', Hayley said. 'Tha-y-nk God!' she added. We all laughed.

The Blue Ridge Mountains or Misty Mountains are part of the Appalachian Mountains and have a range of bluish hues when seen from a distance, despite the blanket of trees over them. Trees put the 'blue' in the Blue Ridge: it comes from the isoprene (a chemical made by plants) released into the atmosphere, which contributes to the characteristic haze around the mountains and their distinctive colour.

What I noticed about The Blue Ridge Parkway was its scenic beauty. I was captivated. It was hard to imagine it running for almost 470 miles through twenty-nine counties in Virginia and North Carolina, which is around half of the length of the United Kingdom.

I looked over, admiring the views and I really felt in touch with nature: it was sheer tranquillity. It was strange that I had once read Bill Bryson's book and witnessing the stunning and atmospheric scenery he described, and it made me feel, I was meant to be here. A sea of oak trees covered the lower elevations and in the high parts, an undulating carpet of conifers covered the mountains distorted by passing clouds. I looked up and wanted to explore the park, despite its dangers and mysterious appearance.

After lunch, we visited the Blue Ridge Parkway Animal Sanctuary and finally saw black bears in abundance, although sadly, in captivity, and they looked smaller than I had imagined. Some of them were even climbing trees. We also saw red deer and cougars, again, in captivity.

Those mesmerising views of the blue misty mountains and the feelings of serenity will always stay with me.

28

Late October 2003

The first of my two British friends came to visit me.

Sandy (my Christian friend), who I turned to last year in my moment of crisis, came to stay for a week. It was her half term and sadly, I had to work, although she knew that before she arrived. We met in a school where we once worked and had developed a good friendship.

We only had one whole weekend together and I felt sorry for her being on her own during the week. She went walking several times, mainly to local stores, and I appreciated her company when I returned home each day.

I tried to leave school as early as I could to spend more time with her. I think I had taken solitude for granted. I collected her on a Saturday evening from Raleigh-Durham Airport and she gawped once she saw the size of my apartment.

Most evenings we stayed local, sometimes venturing into Raleigh to eat at some nice restaurants or looking around small art galleries that, luckily, remained open late.

I had generally observed that most Americans ate food just using their forks, and this strangely irritated me. I eventually embraced it and did it myself at times, especially when eating pasta. In one restaurant, I noticed a man using his knife and fork to cut up his huge steak. Bizarrely, I homed in on this situation as I was curious to know whether he was American or not. I rudely listened to his conversation which turned out to be southern drawl. I hoped he had not noticed my curiosity as I watched him skilfully cut his steak (the size of a calf) into small cubes, taking him fifteen minutes or so.

I cannot explain why I was puzzled and drawn into this steak-dicing experience: perhaps because in England I was used to seeing people cut off one piece of meat at a time and combine it with vegetables. Once he had cut the steak, into what appeared to be twenty equally-sized perfect cubes, he put his knife back down precariously and started using his fork to eat the whole meal. I left the restaurant feeling strangely disappointed and these same images flashed through my mind days later.

Sandy cooked some evenings and we spent a lot of time catching up, watching American TV and laughing. My sofa was big and just as comfortable as my bed, but it was the first time I had slept on it; which I did for the whole week.

As we sat at the table and ate a meal she had cooked, she said, 'They sold tea but I couldn't find any green curry sauce', she giggled, rather annoyingly.

'I wonder how many people round here have actually cooked a Thai green curry. In fact, I wonder how many people around here even cook!'

'Many Americans go out to eat, don't they?' she asked.

'It seems to be that way. I must admit, I cooked more back in London than I do here. I don't know, it just seems cheaper and feels more convenient to eat out. You should see the length of the queue at McDonald's at the weekends – it is unreal and must take ages to get served!'

'Well the meal we ate the other night only came to $28!' Sandy reminded me.

'Really?'

'Yes.' Sandy had a good memory, especially when it came to numbers.

'It seems that everything works out cheaper here – maybe it is just the value of the dollar?'

It was Friday and I was looking forward to spending this weekend with her. 'What shall we do tomorrow?' I asked.

'We could go for a drive a somewhere?'

'Someone at school told me about Busch Gardens in Virginia', I said.

'What is it?'

'A theme-park.'

'I'm not into those scary rides.'

'I am going to force you to go on the big dipper!'

'Noo', she said quietly and femininely – an endearing characteristic of hers.

'Well, we can just have a look around and I won't force you to go on any rides! I think they are supposed to have a nice bird sanctuary there and we could peruse the shops and do luncheon', I said in a pronounced British accent.

'One might go on one of those rides too!' she laughed, albeit nervously.

'I have done some research on Virginia and I would like to see Richmond. It is supposed to have a 'British' feel and you can buy antique glass boxes', she explained.

'Shall we go then?' I asked.

'Yay!'

That was the weekend quickly planned and a third state to visit.

We left quite early on the Saturday morning.

'This is first time we have been out during the day', Sandy pointed out, as we drove down Amelia Church Road and onto the US 70, in bright October sunshine.

I know she had been feeling frustrated with spending most of her days alone that she had come to visit me and I had to go to work. Either way, I felt guilty and in retrospect, I should have taken a day off sick.

Within minutes, I was driving at sixty, heading north, passing interesting road signs: Rocky Mount and Rocky Mount Tarboro. We soon joined the I-95 N, seeing green and white road signs, guiding us to Richmond.

'Do you get confused by all these signs, especially when there are three of them next to each other?' Sandy asked.

'All the time!' We both laughed. 'I think I am getting the hang of it. Three signs mean you are heading towards three places at the same time, and the exits for the places you want will be on that route at some point.' I suddenly noticed a road sign. 'Yay, we are in Virginia!'

I noticed the sign also had a red bird displayed on it. This was the state bird of Virginia, also a cardinal, in red and sitting on a branch of a flowering American dogwood tree (the state tree of Virginia).

'The traffic is light!' she noted.

'Yes, America puts the pleasure back into driving.' I quickly turned my head and smiled at her.

It was so easy to drive and I was expecting to see dogs driving their owners instead; all the dog had to do was press a paw on the gas pedal, sit back and relax with one paw on the wheel and another hanging out of the window and not move for two hours. I wondered why actors always over-emphasise moving the steering wheel in American films – the 'strenuous' part of any journey was getting into or out of the car.

'I have not really experienced much traffic here unless it rains. You get from A to B and it is painless!' I added. 'Did you see that sign?' I blurted out in astonishment.

'No! What did it say?'

'Speed limit enforced by aircraft!'

'You're kidding?' Sandy giggled. 'You mean, planes fly over and watch cars speeding?'

'That's hilarious!' I added.

'Imagine that in England?'

We both stared at each other and laughed for a second as I drove.

'Just don't speed then!'

'Definitely not!'

Just as we spoke, a police car parked at the side of the I-95 pointed a radar gun at me. I glanced down at my speedometer, noticing I was driving just below sixty.

I looked at Sandy.

'Are we are going to jail? she asked sarcastically, as we carried on driving along the autumnal tree-lined interstate, arriving at Busch Gardens in Williamsburg some three hours later.

'I hope not!'

We were greeted at the entrance booths by people with squeaky voices, as if they had been breathing in helium-filled balloons. They told us about the expensive admission prices, and as Sandy blankly refused to go any theme rides, we just paid a minimum entrance fee allowing us to only look around the park.

165

Once inside, we walked down the path until we arrived at the section named 'England'. The houses there were mock-Tudor style, with traditional shops and cafes dotted around, including a fish and chip shop that tempted us both. However, we decided to stop at a cafe for tea and sandwiches instead, and once we had finished, we carried on ambling around.

The park had different 'country' sections, including Italy, Germany, Scotland, Ireland and France, with pretzels served in Germany and pizza in Italy, and there was also a convoluted lake that ran through most of the park.

I liked the 'Lochness Monster' located in the Scottish section and the 'Escape from Pompeii' ride in the Italian section. Theme rides spread through the entire park and depending on which country they were in or near, they had a name or style similar to that country.

We also looked at a bird sanctuary, and saw an American bald eagle, a tawny owl and a Harris hawk, all bigger than I thought. A female bird-keeper held them, wearing a thick leather glove. I had to do a double take as she looked almost identical to the older janitor at my school and I was expected her to say, 'Don't scratch maa floors!'

We started walking back to the entrance.

'Bloody typical of them to have an Irish pub in the Irish part, don't you think?'

'Yes, it was a bit obvious', Sandy replied, as we laughed.

'The French section didn't feel very French either!'

After our whirlwind 'European tour', we left Busch Gardens around 2 p.m..

We walked out of the park and drove onto Richmond, the State Capital of Virginia, which took another hour or so.

The main street in downtown Richmond had a European feel, especially with its cobbled roads, Irish pubs and antique shops that sold glass trinket boxes.

I had enjoyed Sandy's company over the last week and really appreciated her visit. I drove her back to Raleigh-Durham Airport early on Sunday morning, although she became visibly upset when it was time to board her flight. I knew she had been concerned about me

166

last year, but I assured her I was feeling much better, although it was nice that she still cared.

29

Late November 2003

Robbie arrived and he planned to stay for two weeks and I was looking forward to his company. I still felt bad I could not take time off during Sandy's visit but that is one of the restrictions of teaching.

Luckily, for Robbie, I was going to be off for three days for Thanksgiving and we hoped to travel to Atlanta and Washington, DC.

On Sunday I collected him from the usual airport and I was really happy to see him. Once on the highway, he still felt nauseous from his flight and found the experience of me driving to be daunting, as this was the first time he had seen me drive in America.

I had known Robbie for many years and I met him in a job centre that he used to work in, and we just hit it off and became good friends. I had missed his fellowship, his humour and I loved him, just like a brother.

'You've got the hang of this, haven't you!' he said in an affected Mancunian accent, which I had also missed.

We often over-exaggerated our northern accents sometimes in conversation. Robbie was articulate and we loved doing impressions of people: bouncing off each other's comments and shared humour – that is what made our friendship last so long.

We had been through a lot together, since we first met. I missed his warmth and there was nobody else quite like him – I could relate to him. Although I got on well with Ade and had appreciated his friendship since arriving in North Carolina, this was a deeper friendship. Robbie was the type of person who never got bored and I never got bored of him. He enjoyed his own company and was happy staying indoors, relaxing during the day or just watching TV.

Even though I sometimes felt tired from school, we went into Raleigh, most evenings. I also introduced him to Walmart and his first meal at Arby's, although he was not particularly impressed with it.

As our birthdays were just days apart, I wanted to host a joint birthday party to celebrate. I invited fellow Viffers and teachers from school, including two young American teachers: Rachel from Indianapolis and Jessica from another primary school in North Carolina – both of them lived in the same complex.

People arrived early at the party, bringing alcohol and a range of American foods, including homemade pumpkin pie (which I had never eaten before) and lemon meringue pie, cookies and chips (crisps).

Around 7 p.m., the party was in full swing with about fourteen guests, yet the apartment still looked empty. Sadly, there was no sign of Ade – I think he was busy with his new girlfriend – but at least Robbie had already met him.

It felt nice hosting my own party and it was great seeing everyone outside of school enjoying themselves, although the party ended early, around midnight; school was slowly killing us all.

Thanksgiving Day was my first experience of a real American holiday, and although Americans usually celebrate it by eating turkey and reuniting with their respective families, Robbie and I had an alternative way of celebrating: stopping at a MacDonald's before driving to Washington, DC.

We were eager to visit America's capital and, coincidentally, I had also arranged to-see another friend there, who I had met online on a gay website. After around four hours of driving, we arrived and met up with my new friend for lunch at a cafe inside a rather run-down shopping centre. His name was Glen and he was born in Washington, DC, although he had a Peruvian father.

We all got on well and after lunch I said I would come back to visit him again.

After saying goodbye to Glen, Robbie and I drove around, looking for the Capitol Building. Once we had found it, we parked up and took photographs of each other on the famous steps.

We got back into the car and drove to the Supreme Court Building, Washington Monument and then parked the car again and walked around the White House.

I kept my head warm by wearing a beanie, a new article of clothing which seemed popular: it was noticeably colder and getting dark earlier – winter was approaching.

We spent the next couple of days relaxing in my apartment and drove into Raleigh.

The next morning, we woke very early, and took turns driving our epic, eight-hour journey to Atlanta. We certainly felt relieved to see the Peach State signs (a landmark on the epic journey), as we drove on the I-85.

As we approached Atlanta, mid-afternoon, we marvelled at the views of the space-age city, stopping at the side of freeway to take more photographs of the vista against a bright blue Georgian sky. Robbie particularly appreciated the view of Atlanta, as he appreciated American skylines, which looked even more dramatic when illuminated at night.

Lenox Square was bustling with people (there was a noticeably higher black population than Raleigh) and we only really stopped there for a short time because we were tired, cold and hungry.

I really wanted to look at the house were Martin Luther King, Jr, once lived, which had now become a National Historic Site but in the end, we didn't have enough time. We started to feel cold and got back into the car, driving past the Martin Luther King, Jr, Memorial. During the 1960s, Atlanta was a major organising centre of the Civil Rights Movement and where Martin Luther King, Jr did his famous historical speeches.

We drove around the downtown area and while I was admiring a tall skyscraper, I turned a corner, mounted the pavement, and burst the front left tyre. It took a long time to change it and the outside temperature was barely above freezing, numbing my fingers which stuck to the wheel nut, but by sheer luck, I managed it.

Once I had finished, we spotted the golden arches (a welcoming sight in sub-zero temperatures), so I parked the car quickly and we dashed inside McDonald's, saving us from hypothermia – a cheeseburger and piping-hot coffee had never tasted so good! As we drove off, I noticed the back tyre was also punctured, luckily, our 'guardian angels' must have been watching over us as we drove past a nearby garage that was still open, selling cheap tyres for 20 dollars.

We stayed over in a budget motel that evening, on the outskirts of Atlanta, looking more like a 1970s time-warp, and the next day we preferred viewing most of the city from the car due to the cold weather. We kept the heating on full and drove past the Centennial Olympic Park and the Coca Cola Building, and we became really excited driving up and down several times on the Atlanta City Pass, amazed by its sheer size. Atlanta reminded me of *The Jetsons* cartoon – it was just a shame the car didn't fly!

On our way back to North Carolina, we pulled over at a Bojangles' and I convinced Robbie to try grits. He was not overly keen, judging by the expression on his face, and he nearly spat them out on the limp paper plate they had been served on. Following my student's recommendation, I ate them with bacon. I liked the bland taste, although I needed to add several spoons of sugar – sweet and savoury was a new experience! The nutritional information card on the table pointed out grits contained no saturated fats or cholesterol.

The cities of Atlanta and Washington, DC were different to rural North Carolina: no 'rednecks', fewer pick-up trucks, more art galleries and museums, and we managed some walking – a strange experience for me, at least!

I had enjoyed Robbie's good company and wished he could have stayed longer.

30

December 2003

The rest of the semester passed quickly and the Christmas holidays soon approached. VIF sent me return flights to Manchester for the two-week holiday and I was looking forward to spending time with family and friends.

I went to the school Christmas party before I left North Carolina, which was fun and I became acquainted with the expression 'Happy Holidays', even saying it myself at times, but despite it sounding joyous, it seemed to lack a religious feel.

Apart from spending time with family, I visited Manchester, Liverpool and London to catch up with friends, excitedly taking photographs in order to show the students back in North Carolina. Initially it felt strange but walking around everywhere felt 'nice'. The streets and roads seemed compact and familiar; sadly, in North Carolina, I had become too reliant on my car.

There were moments where I would reflect and fully appreciate how lucky I was to have family and friends back in England and my 'other' life in America, suddenly felt far away and surreal. Sometimes it felt as though I had two lives but spending time with my family again made me realise the decision to live in America had been a brave one; that small signature on a piece of paper after the VIF interview had created a life-changing event and opened up a whole world of new experiences.

Having spent the last few months in America, it made me realise England has so much culture, and being away made me understand how much I valued it. I also missed soap operas, music, walking, cups of tea, going to the pub, fry-ups, sarcasm, friends, family, and more importantly, my dad.

I wanted my two weeks in England to be as 'British' as possible: I devoured my first English fry-up and I had forgotten how good proper, brewed tea tasted. I wanted to go to the pub, drink beer, eat cheese and onion crisps, drink red wine and I just couldn't get enough. I hired a small car for a few days and took my dad for high tea but the pinnacle of my visit was eating Christmas dinner. As I looked over at my dad across the table, he looked happy, and that was a special feeling; I knew, deep down, that my place was here and strangely, I had not thought about my American life all day.

All too soon, the Christmas holidays were over. Luckily, I managed to get direct return flights between Manchester and Raleigh. My dad was more upset this time at Manchester airport. It was comforting, yet upsetting, and after reassuring him again, I knew I would be back soon.

I arrived at Raleigh-Durham airport, again sleeping for most of the flight. I was tired of pulling my heavy suitcase trolley around the car park, up and down slopes, as I had forgotten which level I had parked my car on. Stupidly, I left my suitcase and bag unattended and sadly, my mobile phone and camera were taken – and all those memorable photographs. That was not a hurdle, just a case of bad luck.

173

31

The tubs of chocolate I had brought back with me from England took up much of the space in my suitcase but the kids loved them. No words could describe the expressions on their faces as they devoured them.

Some ate while their eyes rolled back, reminding me of sharks eating their prey. American chocolate, nil; English chocolate, one.

I found it bizarre to hear them call chocolate 'candy'. Personally, I found American chocolate had a somewhat 'bitter' taste. Apparently, the milk added to American chocolate goes through a chemical process of breaking down fats producing butyric acid, which stabilises the milk from further fermentation, resulting in a particular 'tangy' taste.

Maybe Americans have come to associate this with the taste of their own chocolate, hence the broad, smiling kids' faces and their many different remarks as they enjoyed the sweeter English chocolate: 'smooth', 'strange candy', 'good candy', 'weird candy', 'bu-dd-ery', 'impressive', 'happenin', 'wow', 'awesome', 'this tastes so good', 'I like it' and 'oh my God!'

Before the block ended, three tubs had been emptied and I had just ruined the appetites of thirty disillusioned 8th graders; but whatever magic those chocolates had, they won me brownie points for the rest of the week.

I had survived my first semester, and things had improved, despite the odd hurdle here and there. The students no longer looked at me like Meerkats, peering out of holes in the ground, each time I spoke. I had started to say pronounce d's instead of t's, especially in words such as 'wa-d-er' (water), 'ci-d-y' (city), and 'compu-d-er' (computer) – sometimes it was less effort to blend in with everyone.

I still had thirteen weeks to go until spring break (the equivalent of our two-week Easter holidays). I knew the semester was going to be tough as the students would have to sit their end of grade examinations

(EOGs). Incidentally, they sat EOGs in math and language arts but not science!

I had a new timetable for this semester and started teaching the Evolution topic in the science block that afternoon and part of me was dreading it.

A girl put her hand up as high as it could go as she stared at me with an expressionless face.

'Yes, Bailey.' This was the challenging question I had been waiting for.

'Aah heard fossils were pla-y-nted by the devil to mis-gaade us from God?' That was a comment I would never forget.

An eerie silence filled the room and thirty more expressionless faces stared at me. My eyes shifted around the room, uncomfortably, and I really wanted to go to my car and drive off into the sunset.

'No one is asking you to believe this is true, Bailey. Fossils have been discovered by people called palaeontologists, and their job is to look for fossils inside rocks.'

'But could someone ha-y-ve put th-e-ym there, on purpose?'

'No Bailey, these fossils are very deep underground.'

'They sti-y-ll could ha-y-ve put th-e-ym there?'

'Who could have put them there?' I asked.

'People who don't believe in God, like scientists.'

She looked around at her friends, as the mood in the room had changed. I was not quite sure if she was serious but as she had a mystified expression, I took it she was.

'The fossils are miles underground, so, it is impossible. Also, I am sure some scientists believe in God.'

'How old are the fossils?' she asked.

Again, I hesitated. I knew from the advice given in orientation that I had to be sensitive to people's beliefs, so I answered vaguely.

'Very old.'

'Are they hundreds of years old?' she asked.

'Older.'

'Thousands?'

'According to scientists, millions!'

I could have heard a pin drop from ten miles away.

175

'But...how?' She genuinely looked baffled.

'Well, it's a theory by scientists. Like I said, you don't have to accept it or believe it.'

'We-y-ll, aah don't believe it.' She folded her arms in defiance.

This generated incensed mumbles across the classroom, as they all started looking at each other. At this point, I really wanted to start singing loudly and slowly, *Happy Talk* by Captain Sensible, while jumping joyfully around the classroom in front of their desks

I could not understand why the study of fossils was not included in the curriculum in this part of America. I was aware certain fundamental religions have views on the age of the Earth, and, which faith people decided to follow, I respected but surely this was educational. Around seventy-nine per cent of people in North Carolina are Christian, and Baptists remain the single largest church in the state.

Knowing this, I was sensitive with my approach but these kids were plainly curious. Another boy, called Mike asked me another question.

'Are fossils animals?' I know they were showing interest but the questioning seemed relentless.

'Yes, they were animals or plants, then they died, got buried in mud and the bones of the animals were replaced with minerals from the rocks and turned into fossils.'

Another girl called Launa, who was usually quiet, put her hand up. Strangely, I had taught another girl in England who looked similar and she was quiet too. It was odd that they were comparable but the American Launa was more confident. In fact, I had generally noticed that American kids had this inbuilt confidence starting at a young age. I am not sure if it was based on American culture, their upbringing, was inherent or a combination of everything. American shyness was 'different' to British shyness. Americans at large seemed more outspoken and knew what they wanted. On many occasions, I had heard the expression 'I want', not, 'I'd like'. Launa, was by no means shy, just quieter than her peers and seemed more aware of others around her. However, she still spoke directly.

'Yes, Launa.'

'Ahh ha-yve tew questions to a-ysk. The Baable never mentions dinosaurs, so they obviously weren't created by God!' she exclaimed.

'I can't answer that, Launa.'

'That's faane. Maa second question is about fossils. They can come from pla-y-nts too, right?' These were not really questions but seemingly delivered statements.

'Plants can become fossils too in a similar way as animals do but plants get buried in mud and just turn into fuels as they get changed by the pressure and heat under the Earth's crust. The fossils of small animals and plants can become fossil fuels and are found in inside rock.'

'Yew mean, we are pudd-in' bits of dinosaurs in our cars?' one boy asked.

I thought at that point, I was opening up a can of worms and worried how this conversation was going to pan out.

'No, we will talk about that another time.' I really wanted to get them to do some work but they were inquisitive.

Another small girl, called Kyra, raised her hand and asked, 'So when pla-ynts get trapped, they daa too?'

'Yes, they die too.'

'Is that because pla-ynts cannot get any more sunlaaght?' Kyra asked sensibly.

'Pla-ynts don't need sun', an outspoken Brian said.

'Y-es they do, you re-tard!' Kyra quipped.

'I also think we need to have further discussions about what defines a 'retard'!' I had heard the word used liberally which made me feel uncomfortable.

'Sir, do pla-ynts need sun to stay alaave?' a boy called Joshua asked.

'Yes, they need the sun to photosynthesise. You might have heard that word before?'

'What is tha-yt?' Mike asked.

'Well, we can talk about that another time, in more detail but plants need different things to photosynthesise. Does anyone know what else they need?'

'Wa-d-er?' a small girl called Tiff, blurted out.

'Correct!'

177

A boy called Tyler eagerly put his hand up, looked serious and appeared ready for a discussion. 'Yes?' I asked.

'Can I get wa-d-er?'

'NO!'

The entire class laughed, looked round at him and then, back at me. 'What else do plants need to photosynthesise?' I asked.

Tyler put his hand up again. 'Can I get wa-d-er?'

'I think you will survive without water for a few more minutes.'

'But, Mr Woo-ood, I need wa-d-er!'

I adopted a Hugh Grant accent again. 'You don't need water, right at this very moment.' I tried hard not to smirk.

'I need wa-der.' Tyler was about to burst into tears.

I continued ignoring him, although I was feeling quite exasperated that he would not actually be quiet. So, hard-nosed, I carried on.

'Well, plants need sun, water and ...?' I was interrupted again, for further demands of water from Tyler. This was obviously a wind-up. 'Tyler, look, you don't need wa-d-er. You can wait for a minute, right?' My American spin made everyone laugh. 'As I was just about to explain, plants need ...?'

'Aah really need wa-d-er Mr Woo-ood, seriously, aah do.'

'No, you don't, Tyler Manning!' He was about to go into nuclear meltdown.

If I had been David Banner, my eyes would have turned green with that strange sound effect before his transformation into the Hulk.

I then said, in a raised voice, 'Okay. I will arrange for you to go on trip to the Sahara Desert and then you will DEFINITELY need water!' A sudden joy filled Tyler's face.

'Yew mean, aah can go to the Sahara Desert?'

Louna looked at Tyler. 'You re-tard!'

'Louna!'

'Sorry, Mr Woo-ood. He's stu-pid!'

I exhaled and closed my eyes. I think Louna was the only one to understand my sarcasm. 'Tyler, go and get some wa-d-er and by the way, you have detention.' I was now annoyed.

They all immediately burst into hysterical laughter.

'When you come back we might not be here!'

'Oh, where will y'all be?'

'THE SAHARA DESERT?' the whole class shouted out and laughed.

I sniggered and allowed him to leave the room. He looked around trying to seek approval from his classmates, who shook their heads in shame.

'I thought you were dying of thirst. GO!' He pathetically left the room.

'Is he the class clown or what?' I asked the class.

'No, just the cla-yss idiot, Mr Woo-ood!' Mike exclaimed. That was a slick response. Despite Tyler's behaviour bordering on annoyance and hilarity, putting the onus on him had taken me out of the spotlight. However, it was just what I needed to hear in order to see the funny side of this situation. Once again, the whole class burst into laughter.

'You're funny Mr Wooooooood', Kyra added, as she smiled innocently.

'Okay, kids, let's do some work on…fossils!'

Many shuffled in their seats eager to work and picked up books from the floor next to their desks as I looked around and smiled at them. A couple of them looked up at me and quietly giggled. One boy called Luke, who had never spoken since my first day of teaching, looked at me, put his thumb up, nodded and smiled. I think I just gained some respect and I quite enjoyed the banter.

Tyler sheepishly scuttled back into the room, sitting down at his desk. I think he half-expected a rapturous applause upon his return.

'The class idiot is back, Sir.' I discreetly started laughing with them. Within a minute or so, they all continued to work quietly. Tyler looked around the room again for affirmation but some just shook their heads.

I did notice one student looking up at me, as I leaned forward in my chair. I smiled back at him, feeling a sense of satisfaction, as the rest busily answered their questions.

The weekend arrived and on the Friday evening, I went out with Tee, to the local movie theatre in Smithfield to watch *Cold Mountain*, a film about the Civil War, ironically set in North Carolina. The movie

179

depicted most of the scenery there: stunning in the summer and Christmas card scenes in the winter. Nicole Kidman acted superbly with a southern drawl. Her mannerisms imitated North Carolinians: innocence, gentleness and friendliness.

North Carolina is a beautiful state but I really wanted to venture further afield. Some Viffers had talked about visiting Miami at Easter and asked me to go, although I would have to see how my finances would stretch at the time. I definitely wanted to see more of America.

The weather was growing colder and Johnston County was on snow alert. My beanie had become an essential and permanent fixture. There had been some flurries of snow, and on one occasion, the kids did not come into school as many arrived by the school bus but the bus could not be driven through the snow in other areas of the county. The drivers of the stereotypical American yellow school buses were similar to taxi drivers in the UK. The driver owns the bus, but is not insured to drive kids in hazardous conditions – their parents could sue to the hilt, in the event of an unfortunate accident.

The capture of Saddam Hussein was constantly on *Channel 1 News* each morning. Personally, I was more worried about this situation than ever before as terrorism certainly is a mind-set that is difficult to change and the Americans seemed quite adamant that they were at 'war'.

Americans also did not seem to worry about showing Saddam Hussein being taken out from the hole where he was caught – this humiliation of their leader could have encouraged his network to carry out more terrorist attacks in the US, if not in other parts of the world.

Americans have belief in and take pride in their nation, and this is reflected in many different aspects of American culture: the pledge, American flags on lawns, American flags etched on the rear windscreens of pick-up trucks, on TV, everyday conversations and just a general belief across the whole country that 'America is the greatest'. From what I gathered from being there, Americans have a general attitude that 'anything is possible' and if they want it, they get it.

I spoke to Glen late Friday evening on the phone. 'Hey, what are you doing this weekend?'

'I have nothing planned.'

'Fancy coming to DC?'

'Are you sure? It's pretty short notice!'

'It's actually Martin Luther King Day tomorrow. Maybe I could show you around DC?'

'Yeah, that would be great. I'll try and get there for around one.'

32

As the traffic flowed along the I-95 N, I arrived in DC around 1 p.m. The efficiency of the American infrastructure was admirable. I met up with Glen in a coffee shop, and later he showed me around his compact apartment in Dupont, which was within easy walking distance of DC's three main areas: Dupont Circle, Georgetown and Adams Morgan.

Adams Morgan reminded me of Islington in North London: multicultural, interesting restaurants and quirky cafes dotted around its many streets, although DC was -10 °c; a temperature I had not experienced, and after a while, it was difficult to walk around without feeling uncomfortably cold. All I wanted to do was be indoors, drinking hot chocolate. I could not imagine life without my beanie, scarf and gloves, complete with a zipped-up snorkel jacket with a furry hood over the beanie – protection from the harsh elements. Glen told me snowploughs sometimes clear the snow that is piled high on sidewalks – I had yet to witness this scene.

He seemed proud of his city and began telling me that Washington, DC, is not in a state but is a federal district, formally known as the District of Columbia, commonly called 'Washington', 'the District', or simply 'DC', although most of its inhabitants use the latter term. He also explained that commuters from the surrounding Maryland and Virginia suburbs temporarily increase the city's population to more than a million during the working week. DC was named in honour of President George Washington and was founded in 1791 to serve as the nation's capital. Glen's knowledge of American history was an attractive trait!

In contrast to the loud personalities American actors often portray, Glen was a quietly spoken man: humble, yet, despite his introverted approach on life, he had an inner confidence which shined through as he talked and began to open up. I could sense he had been let down and he later told me, he too, had been hurt in the past. He seemed guarded, as was I, so we both decided that developing a good friendship was the best option, for now, and if anything further developed between us, then that would be a bonus.

Later that day, we visited the National Art Gallery where most of the exhibitions were underground, including a large wing displaying Dutch and Italian Renaissance works. There were three small glass pyramids (of a similar design to the one at the Louvre) which you could look through from an underground tunnel connecting the two sections of the art gallery.

During a brief visit to the Air and Space Museum, we walked around a replica of Air Force One, seemingly gigantic, which flies the US president around, although it was difficult to conceive it actually flying. We also boarded Concorde and, finally, we looked at spacecraft: a moon buggy and we went inside the Skylab. Both seemed 'primitive' as they were made of metal bolted together and it was difficult to imagine the Skylab hurtling through Earth's atmosphere at over 500 miles per hour. We also saw a model of the Space Shuttle in the NASA museum, which appeared a lot smaller than I had imagined.

Glen formally invited me (as his 'guest') to dinner on the Saturday evening with some of his friends. The couple hosting the dinner were Jewish. They explained the significance of eating bread and drinking wine – a blessing, customary at every meal. I was told a man should not break bread for visitors unless he eats with them, and I was that visitor. They put salt on the bread and although it was interesting, it took him twenty minutes to explain. It had something to do with Kabbalah: salt, which is bitter, represents divine severity, and bread, the staff of life, represents divine kindness. Lastly, the couple prayed and sang. Meanwhile, I smiled and nursed my hunger pains!

The meal ended with three flavours of ice cream for desert. In the end, I ate so much food. I do not know how I physically managed it, as the following day, we ate at IHOP (International House of Pancakes) around lunchtime. In IHOP, I ate four pancakes (each one the diameter of an extra-large dinner plate), two eggs (sunny-side up), chicken strips and fries, waffles, maple syrup with more eggs: not a very low cholesterol, healthy meal and I felt gluttonous after eating so much. I must admit, I was becoming partial to the sweet and savoury experience and liked the combination of eggs and maple syrup, a very 'American thing!'

I felt I was going to explode and it took ten minutes to waddle back to the car parked just outside the entrance doors. Feeling bloated to a new extreme, I loosened my belt while sitting uncomfortably in Glen's car. As Glen drove away, my breathing shallowed, my fingers tingled and I felt 'out of sorts'. My distended stomach seemed to push upwards into my chest and I think I knocked ten years off my life. I felt sweaty and even pressing the electric window button felt like an effort. We arrived back at Glen's apartment, and walking from the car required a certain 'skill'.

After a cup of tea and staring blankly at the TV screen as our stomachs started to shrink, I looked at Glen who smiled and suddenly said, 'Paul, you look really happy.'

'Because I had a nice day and being with you has felt great.' Glen flashed his white straight teeth. 'It feels like we have been partying all day and night.'

'The-old-you-is-coming-back,' Glen said in precisely metered tones. I confirmed with a huge grin.

'We have done a lot today', Glen announced.

'Yes, we have.'

'What's been your favourite part of this weekend?'

'Erm … being with you.'

'You sweet-talker!'

'I know, although, I could do with a quick walk before I head back to North Carolina.'

'We could walk to the Spanish Steps?'

'Are they far?'

'About fifteen minutes from here, I think?'

'Okay, I just think my bed might collapse when I lie on it tonight.' Glen laughed at my remark.

We wrapped up warm, left the apartment block, as it was chilly outside. We slowly walked across a bridge towards the Spanish Steps.

'You like DC, don't you?' Glen asked.

'Yes. I like being here.'

We arrived at the Spanish Steps. I looked around and we walked down some of the steps to admire the lion head fountain.

'I like that,' I said.

'I think it had to be rebuilt due to a car crash about four years ago.'

'Oh no! You are full of facts and figures, aren't you?'

'At least I am not full of shit!' I suddenly laughed in response.

'You know something?'

'What?'

'I visited the Spanish Steps when I was in Rome last year.'

'Did you?'

'Yeah.'

'How strange. I'm sure the ones in Rome are more elaborate.'

'That's Italy for you!'

'How else do they compare?' Glen asked.

I looked back at the water fountain and the over-hanging leafless branches of the trees before turning to look at Glen who was staring at me in the dimly-lit area.

'Maybe, it's more, 'romantic' here?'

'Why's that then?'

I looked straight into Glen's eyes, who then moved forward and confidently kissed me. 'That was nice.' I quietly said as I blushed.

'It was for me, too.'

I looked down and held his hands.

'I feel surprisingly revitalised.'

'I know one thing?'

'What's that?'

'You're looking especially handsome right now,' Glen said.

'Maybe we should go back to yours?'

'Maybe we should,' Glen replied and I grinned at him as we set off.

I drove back to North Carolina later that evening and felt content during my journey as I reflected on the weekend and how busy it had been.

185

Once I arrived back very late at my apartment, in Clayton, I took my time to wash my face and change, then lay on my bed thinking that nobody at school knew about my secret weekends away in DC. It would just be another normal day in the classroom tomorrow.

I switched the bedside lamp off, turned over looking into the darkness of the apartment but didn't feel alone, and as my eyes adjusted, I noticed the bedroom door ajar in front of me letting in moonlight from the living room and before I fell asleep, I thought about an expression Robbie once said after my relationship ended with Nick.

'As one door closes, another one opens.'

33

School was going like clockwork and students in a new class I was teaching, who had seen me around or had spoken to me in the hall, mainly wanted to hear me talk. In some ways, it was flattering, as they wanted to know exactly where I was from, what music and TV programmes I liked, and so on, but at times, it felt intrusive.

Overall, they were nice kids and I had warmed to them quickly in the short time I had been there. At times, I felt like I was an 'exhibit' at school, or at the bank, or at Walmart, in fact everywhere I had been. Often, people would overhear me and could tell immediately by my accent that I was British. Sometimes, I felt like a novelty act.

However, 'knowing' more about me in this more personal way, gave this new class more confidence (and this worked both ways) as they asked more probing questions about the UK in the first lesson than the other two classes had done for the whole first semester. Throughout my teaching career, developing good working relationships with students has been one of my strengths, but this class seemed a little 'over-familiar', although they were not aware of this.

I met one new student who stared at me as she twitched and who apparently rolled along walls. I had yet to witness this 'wall-rolling' which generated interesting discussions among staff, and there were rumours her mum and dad were really her mum and brother. Although these were just rumours, there was something not quite right about her.

The new class asked me what my favourite animals were. Again, I wrote 'grey wolf' on the white board – deliberately spelling it in the Anglican version, only to provoke another reaction and instantly, they corrected me but although I was amused, this time, I stood my ground.

My spelling created hysteria among the class. Typically, they asked me to pronounce 'aluminium' and 'February'. Ironically, they had spelling bees each week in language arts!

I blurted out in a southern drawl, 'alu-min-um' and I pronounced the 'um' as 'uuuuuum' and Feb- u-ary, placing emphasis on my southern drawl. You would have thought they had been inhaling canisters of laughing gas.

'Please say it your way again Mr Wooood!'

I was indeed, a novelty act, and very deliberately pronounced the words in my best British accent, generating endless laughter and it was difficult not to join in – I had become an 'entertainer'.

I had not realised Americans also emphasised 'u' more in their words: alUminUm and FebUaRy had even more emphasis with the 'r's and I had difficulty understanding ill and pill, which they pronounced as 'eel' and 'peel'. However, they still pronounced 'peel' (as in orange peel) as, 'peel'. They both sounded the same and it all became quite confusing.

I often imitated their accent, speaking in an affected southern drawl when I could, but most did not notice or looked at me as if I was still talking in British English.

After years of teaching in London, my accent had 'softened' and had become 'slower' due to the fusion of regional accents. I did often wonder how they would have understood me if I still had my strong Lancashire accent. Sometimes, I felt slightly frustrated on my drives home thinking about the language barriers that were present even though I was in America, an English-speaking country. Initially, I had the impression the UK and America would be similar but living in America, made me realise that they were in fact very different, especially in the southern states.

For the most part, my drive from work each day was relaxing, mainly because the sunsets were stunning, giving me an opportunity to reflect, or to listen to modern country music which I had grown to appreciate.

When the highways were quiet, I felt lonely out on the wide, open roads, especially when I left early. Twice a day, it was just me and my car on the same journey each way which involved no thought processes. However, I enjoyed this time alone and the car had become my 'friend': dependable, reliable and always there.

The following day in school, two representatives from VIF visited the principal and had a meeting with me. They said the principal said 'nice things' about me and they were just checking on how I was coping at school and with the programme. They asked me if I had made any decisions on next year and they said VIF would prefer me to stay at the same school. Part of me wanted to, as I felt settled and had adapted to this 'American life', and, I was half way through the school year and, maybe, half way though my personal journey. But I knew this 'American life' could not last forever.

Sometimes, it was hard to make decisions on anything: North Carolina, Washington, DC, the UK, or staying with my dad. I liked everything but being in America had taught me one thing: I had coped alone, although, at times, I had felt 'lost'. Going to America had definitely been a good decision, as had going to Italy, and I was glad to have made a connection with North Carolina back then. It was in fact, a parallel journey: an important personal journey and a physical journey in miles.

It was the weekend again and I was looking forward to pottering around and going for a drive. I wanted to spend some time in my apartment and not just use it as place to eat and sleep. Although fellow Viffers had invited me again to the Irish pub in Raleigh on Saturday evening, I liked the idea of choice and not having to go just for the company of others. I was starting to appreciate my own company, in a different part of the world, and I didn't feel lonely, anxious or depressed. I had arrived at a 'new place' in my life. I had accepted my loneliness, I wasn't fighting against it – I had changed.

I decided I wanted to drive, I wanted to be free again and I wanted to 'own' the road. There was nothing ahead but a flat quilt of yellow, green and white fields and an endless inviting horizon. Every so often, I would see another massive expanse of cotton fields or cornfields and water towers, and ten miles later, more of the same or sometimes, a remote wooden chapel; it was all 'familiar' scenery, repeating itself, every ten miles or so. I seemed to drive past the same farm three times, going around in a twenty-mile circle. Again, I felt lost but nothing really mattered – I felt happy.

There seemed to be a million miles of emptiness and as the miles clocked up, I drove countless more. They were not just miles but as the

189

significant numbers increased, so did my level of happiness, as if my emotions were measurable, on a continuous ascending scale. Maybe these numbers were also minutes; with each minute that had gone by I was a minute closer to finding Paul Wood.

I listened to the loud music, drowning out the engine noise. I watched the four lanes ahead, opening wider before me, allowing me through, and as I drove, they closed up, as if the road was unzipping ahead and zipping up behind me. The lanes moved yet I stayed in the same position, and sometimes the side hedges appeared blurred - I was in motion and my life had changed in the last few months: love, work, friendships, culture and nature, everything different yet everything that I could see through the windscreen and in the far distance remained still and had probably remained unchanged for many years. I slowed down and pulled over at the next exit, driving slowly and carefully along an uneven narrow dirt track. I wanted to stop the car and take a closer look at the cotton fields.

I got out of the car. The plain was flat and featureless but I wanted to take photographs to capture its serenity. The sun was already high in the sky but the air was crisp. In front of me lay yet another thousand square miles of cotton fields and cornfields.

I got back into my car and drove on, passing another wooden chapel. Where was I going? I didn't know, but I just wanted to drive and feel liberated. I was that bird, flying free into the vastness of the Carolinian countryside.

I pulled over again, on another dusty side road; there was another wooden chapel, its white paint old and rustic, peeling yet gleaming in the bright sunshine. Was this the same one as I had seen before? Had I driven round in another circle? Had I not realised, or did I not really care where I was going? I looked over, in the opposite direction. There was nothing, apart from the ceaseless movements of cotton plants and a few cars driving in the far distance.

I looked to my left and there was an abandoned rusty-red car with a missing headlight in front of an old run-down wooden shed. The lonely car was covered in layers of brown-red rust – an iconic image of a vehicle that had stood the test of time and weather, against the archetypal backdrop of rural North Carolina.

190

I stared straight ahead, beyond the car, deeper into a cotton field: the plants moved slowly in the wind, making noises and as I looked and listened more closely I saw a dance of ripples on the surface of a million cotton plants that waved in the gentle breeze and quietly rustled. As I imagined each one attached to a small bell, I could hear thousands of bells jingling with different notes which seem to transform into chiming sounds of a glockenspiel, as if I was in a trance yet a strange calmness filled my body and mind. It was the music within nature surrounded by a stillness of natural simplicity – stunning, serene and untouched. No people, no talking: just singing voices of cotton plants, with big buds of cotton in the foreground, blending into a blanket layer of snow-like fuzziness in the distance, as I stared, lost in thought. Each cotton plant stood alone, fragile and free, yet they all swayed in unison, moving with their own rhythm – thousands whispering to each other. This was beauty: kind and gentle. This was freedom – no pain, no feelings and no memories and nothing but peace and tranquillity, being in tune with nature.

I thought how upset I had been last year, how much pain and despair I had gone through and how alone I had felt. I was alone again, but there was no pain – it was a comforting loneliness and everything made sense. I did not have to interact with anyone. I was in a situation I had created.

The feelings I had harboured were not Nick's fault and it had taken time and that much distance to realise it. I had to take responsibility for how I once felt and that I was the one who had to change and accept things as they were. That moment in time, being alone and standing there in the middle of those cotton fields, was an experience I will never forget: it touched me deeply and it transformed me.

I realised everything had its time in this world, including myself and I had to make the most of life. Everything looked beautiful and this was my new reality.

I looked deeper into the cotton plants and it seemed like a dream. Each cotton plant was alive and I could feel their energy, their promise, each one grown from a seed into a new and short life for some greater purpose. Every single problem in life is a seed of an opportunity for some greater benefit or a wider range of possibilities keeping alive the excitement and adventure of life. Those cotton buds would soon be gone: short lives ended by machinery – destroyed yet transformed.

I wondered how many people had worked those fields in the past, picking cotton and existing in painful circumstances that were beyond their control. The plants seemed to bow their heads, respectfully, creating an open space, allowing me inside their world. I remained silent and stared. There I saw a group of transparent ghost-like figures of African-American women, and their young children, picking cotton. The women wore long dresses and white aprons, and silently and gracefully placed cotton buds into overladen baskets strapped around their waists, looking humble and gentle, appearing to move in slow motion, bathed in the golden light.

One young woman bowed down while picking a cotton bud, stopped and gently looked up with her kind, beautiful face. She waved slowly, smiling with tears in her eyes. Slavery was all around her: present in her world yet a moment in history in mine. The sadness I had experienced in comparison to hers was nothing and strangely, she made me feel happy.

How could humans be so cruel yet nature be so kind? My eyes looked at her and she saw me, she knew I was there, she saw my sadness and I saw hers. She was trapped, yet I was free. My arms stretched out and so did hers, we wrapped them around each other, entwined and slowly we turned and spiralled up into the sky like wisps of smoke. I looked deep into her eyes, her sorrow gave me strength, and she spoke like a cold whispering wind: 'you're free'. I tried to speak but no words would come out. I could not breathe.

I had entered a spiritual world and I felt the presence of God, just like I did when I was praying in the Vatican but this time it was overwhelming. I could not speak, I could not breathe, I could not move. This feeling was too much but I wanted more. Had God guided me here, to this time, to this place? Was she an angel? Was the picture of the rusty old car in the cotton field in my mind as I prayed in the Vatican City, this rusty car in this cotton field – was I meant to be here and feel like this: maybe this had to be part of my journey? Just for a moment, she was free from the burdens of slavery but I was now free from the burdens of pain and she was the one who had released me.

I opened my eyes as the wind caused each cotton plant to dance wildly and the cotton field became a moving sea of soft white buds once more and in the foreground stood the rusty old car. I looked harder but she had vanished. I longed to see her, if only for another second. I could not save her but she saved me, a ghost from the past, an illusion yet somehow, she had felt very real. The ethereal scene in sepia colours and the ghostly figurines disappeared as the cotton plants closed ranks to protect their memories, waving in the wind and waving goodbye – she was gone, forever. There was nothing but I had felt everything. She had cured me, she had set me free and I was no longer afraid, I knew what she had said to me, but I could not explain. I came here, to this particular cotton field at this particular moment and I came in search of a meaning for my life and she had given it to me.

The cotton fields had directed me here and they had magic in them. They knew, and I knew my journey was over.

I looked up slowly at the clear blue sky, as stinging tears rolled down my cheeks. I guardedly glanced back at my waiting car. I looked back at the cotton field. I wanted her to come back, to see her face, to hear her voice, to have that feeling, to relive that moment, to ask her name, to thank her, to say goodbye. Another tear rolled down my cheek.

This was my present and my reality. Should I carry on driving or was it now time to go home? Should I keep thinking about what I saw or forget her pain, her sorrow, the love of those innocent people, deep inside those protective fields, a history of suffering and sadness hidden by the simplicity and beauty of nature? I looked again, into the emptiness: waiting for her to return, waiting for her smile but there was nothing, just a field of cotton plants swaying freely, a car which had stood the test of time and a tall water tower standing alone, looking down at me against a cold blue sky.

As I walked towards my car, I stopped to look back at the cotton field, and then at the country lane that guided me here, from nowhere.

193

That day, that spiritual moment defined me, and I knew my personal journey had ended.

34

The snow began falling, gently at first and then in clumps, covering the ground quickly, much to the delight of everyone at the school.

I am sure it is not an easy decision for those in charge to close a school when it snows, and I am certain authorities are only thinking about the health and safety of everyone, yet I could not help enjoy the feeling of spontaneity and sheer delight of an unanticipated day off. The combination of having to decide what to do but also enjoying the surprise is a real treat considering life is often quite planned and regimented; and it is strange that we have no control over the weather yet it has control over us.

The cars in the school car park slowly and cautiously drove away in the heavy blizzard and I felt vulnerable as my car skidded – a pickup truck would have come in useful! – and the journey home took over an hour. It is unfathomable how frozen water has the potential to create chaos, or, more drastically, injury or death.

Driving up the steep slope of Amelia Church Road and into the housing complex proved tricky, but once I arrived back at my apartment, I turned the heating onto maximum and within minutes it became a tropical paradise.

After watching TV and drinking several cups of tea, I walked into the bedroom, sat at my desk and decided to send a few emails home and pay some bills. I looked out of the window and the snow had eased. I then decided to venture outside for a walk in the woods behind Amelia Village. The freshly fallen snow looked like a typical Christmas card scene, complete with magical icicles hanging from tree branches. Dressed in typical winter attire yet again, I wandered around the winter wonderland through the crunchy snow, taking several photos of the icicles hanging like stalactites.

As I trudged through the ankle-deep snow, I remembered sunbathing by the swimming pool at the complex and complaining about how hot it was! I had noticed that conversations about the

195

weather seemed common, just like in the UK, but Americans talked about weather problems as if World War III was imminent. The weather had a big impact upon car drivers as there did not seem to be any public transport. Everyone else who works in colleges, government buildings, stores and many manufacturing companies can arrive two-hours late, yet teachers and students need to be in their classrooms at 7.30 a.m.

Once the snow had cleared, school was back to normal the following day and a busy semester was quickly passing. With just three months left until the end of the school year, there was still a lot of teaching to do. The students finished earlier than in the UK, and soon the pressure of the EOGs would begin – the equivalent of English students preparing for their SATS. The major difference in America was that if students failed math or language arts, they had to attend summer school. If the kids in Johnston County failed two subjects, they could not attend summer school but had to repeat the entire year – presumably an embarrassing situation for some. As a result, there were some sixteen-year olds in the 8th grade. In addition, if they had five or more absences within a nine-week period, they failed the year and had to retake it. Personally, I believed this to be a good way to motivate the students to attend school and maybe British schools should adopt similar policies. Parents had been emailing me directly – something I had not experienced that much in British state schools. It was essential that I kept my school notes (which show what homework is set) updated daily, as it was easy to fall behind.

The good thing was that you could select pieces of homework to count towards their report grades each semester and the majority of the grade for each subject was based on homework. It was best to grade little and often rather than doing a stack of it all in one go just before the grade cards were due to be released, as you would end up hitting a crisis point.

It appeared that teaching positions in North Carolina were relatively insecure because the principal sent out a form asking staff if they wished to stay on for the next academic year: this helped with staffing and budgeting. I could not imagine this situation in British schools – it would create anarchy, although more schools in the UK are employing people under fixed-term contracts, mainly due to financial constraints.

Schools in North Carolina celebrated Black History Month, commonly known as African-American History Month. An article was written about me in the local newspaper, propelling me to 'stardom'. I told the principal that we had commemorated Black History Month in English schools I had worked at and he liked the idea.

I asked my students to compose a PowerPoint presentation in the 'wireless lab', a new concept where the laptops were not connected by wires to the Internet – American technology was way ahead of that in the UK. The students researched an African-American scientist of their own choice.

The local press visited the school while the students researched in the lab and they took photographs of the backs of their heads. They interviewed one student, although they also mentioned some of the other students' names. Only my surname was included in the article, which was how they did things in America. It seemed strange, but I had noticed they used just people's surnames a lot in magazines or on the TV when reporting about celebrities – there was a recent news report about Sandra Bullock, who was constantly referred to as 'Bullock'.

One of the students researched Garret Augustus Morgan, an African-American who invented the first traffic light in 1877. I had told the reporter I had 'no idea' who invented the stoplight but I was 'delighted' to find out it had been invented by an African-American man.

'Black History Month is also celebrated in the UK, and this includes people from Caribbean and Asian countries', I said to the reporter.

'Asian countries?' the reporter asked, looking baffled.

'Yes, people from India or Pakistan.'

'We tend to call Chinese, Japanese and Vietnamese people 'Asian' but Indian and Pakistan are separate nationalities', he said.

197

'In the UK, we tend to say Chinese not Asian.'

'Really?'

'Yes, if someone is applying for a new job, they usually have to complete an equal opportunities' form. If they are originally from India, Pakistan or Bangladesh, they are categorised as Asian.'

The reporter looked surprised. Even though he was correct, factually (China and Japan are countries in Asia, as are India, Pakistan and Bangladesh), categorising all these races as Asian seemed very generalised, and I was not used to hearing the term used in this way.

'The next time I go out for a Chinese meal in England, maybe I should say to my friends, 'Fancy an Asian?'.' He smiled back at me but I was not sure if he thought I was being literal. He then looked over at the children busily doing their research while the photographer took more shots for his article.

The people who lived in Amelia Village were mainly white people, and most of the teachers in my school were white female Americans. I had noticed there were three main divisions of races among students: white, African-American and Mexican, and there were no Indian or Pakistani students (what I would call Asian), or Chinese students.

There were not many Indian takeaways or Chinese restaurants in the suburbs, although they offered a wide variety of menus in the food hall at Crabtree Valley Mall and there was a limited choice in downtown Raleigh. I did miss the choice of restaurants available in London.

The inhabitants of the suburbs around Raleigh were mainly white and most local restaurants, or those just off the I-95 or US 70, served the same typically American fast-food, in concrete buildings of the same design and layout everywhere you went: Subway, Dairy Queen, Arby's, Taco Bell, Bojangles', Wendy's, Zaxby's and Char-Grill. Eating in Arby's in different locations felt as if I had not driven anywhere as the chain restaurants looked identical (even though I only needed to drive two or three miles to get to the next fast-food village).

These food villages were only accessible by car and many of them were just places that served a different form of burger. However, Taco Bel served a variety of Tex-Mex foods, including tacos, burritos,

198

quesadillas, nachos and many have good-value menu items. It was easy to add inches to your waistline and receive a surprising amount in change from a ten-dollar bill!

I went to Taco Bell with Hayley and Tee after school – this was becoming a habit. The restaurant always seemed busy (does anyone cook in North Carolina?). After arriving, I picked up a heavy, two-foot-wide plate and piled on enough salad to feed a whole family of six, and this was just a starter! I noticed other people doing this too, thinking they were being healthy, only to watch a gallon of blue cheese dressing being poured over their lettuce leaves, surely adding 10,000 calories at least?

Everyone in the restaurant was white and every booth contained groups of people, and I could hear the sudden cries of new-born babies or kids running around, laughing or playing: a haven for the average white American family. On one occasion, a group of five young male African-Americans entered and waited to be seated by a waitress. The whole restaurant went quiet and nobody dared to look round (everyone obviously thought they were going to be shot dead!) I casually observed the people sitting opposite me, devouring their over-sized burritos, as they cautiously looked up.

I looked around and then at Hayley and whispered.

'Has everyone just gone quiet in here or is it just me?' She looked uncomfortable and embarrassed.

I had noticed this before, in an IHOP in South Carolina, when a similar situation had unfolded. There was an underlying tension due to racism, not just in North Carolina but in other states I had visited. I suddenly remembered Busch Gardens: everyone was white there too and then I had a flash-back to the McDonald's I had been to in downtown Atlanta. McDonald's burgers were served by African-Americans to African-Americans: a clear-cut division of burgers and races – 99-cent cheeseburgers for African-Americans and $8 burgers for white Americans.

I suddenly thought about some of the children I was teaching. The Mexican children did not appear to mix with the other students – they seemed to be 'invisible' and did not draw attention to themselves. Maybe they were born in the USA but their parents might be illegal immigrants, although I did not want to generalise. Many of the children came from poor backgrounds but it seemed, the poorest of these were African-American children, despite the majority of the children being white, although I did not sense any racial tension in the school. One African-American girl I taught in particular, seemed to have so much going against her in general – racism and poverty, yet she strived to be a good student, working harder than most of her peers. She braved a smile each day and worked conscientiously despite not being the brightest of students and the challenges she faced in her family, in society and possibly, in her future. I wondered what type of burger she would be buying once she was grown up?

At the weekend, I was invited to attend a Baptist church near Clayton. I noticed straight away that the Minister was constantly cracking jokes, and surprisingly his attire was as equally relaxed - dressed in jeans and a jumper, just like everyone in the entire congregation. For some reason, I had expected a welcoming black gospel choir belting out hymns, just like the *Sister Act* film, rocking from side to side behind the altar. However, an all-white congregation sang and there was not a single African-American in sight. Where did African-American people sing and worship, in separate churches or in the poorer areas of North Carolina?

I remembered that I had sensed a racial divide in England, at my first school in south-west London in 1995 where I had observed white and black teachers sitting on opposite sides of the staffroom. I felt uneasy about that then, and would sometimes deliberately sit on the 'black side' rather than the 'white side' of the staff room during break times, like I was in the middle of some kind of human chess game about to start. Teachers would often refer to other people as 'black' or 'white' and I remembered over-hearing a conversation between a group of black teaching assistants sat behind me, on my first day and they were obviously unaware that I was a new teacher.

'Is that new science teacher black or white?'

'White, I heard.'

'He'll get on with his boss then.'

That statement saddened me and made me feel conscious of my

race and colour more than at any other time in my life, apart from when I had gone into an all-black environment in that McDonald's in Washington, DC, where I was then in a minority. Bizarrely, inner city schools in DC have the highest number of African-American students at the poorest public schools and the lowest number in the richest private schools. I guess there are parallels with London but the categories of black and poor and white and rich seemed more obvious here, from grass roots level of a school in rural North Carolina to standing in that McDonald's queue in the heart of the capital city of America, in a country that is supposed to be, the Greatest nation on Earth.

I thought more about the words of the American pledge: 'I pledge allegiance to the Flag of the United States of America, and to the Republic for which it stands, one Nation under God, indivisible, with liberty and justice for all.' From what I had seen, felt and heard, I really did not see justice for all? Mexican kids even had to say it but they did not mix with the white children or the African-American children for that matter – a separate entity. I thought about the Ku Klux Klan again yet, years later it still seemed white America, was inherently racist, and nobody wanted to talk about it. I did not think America had a problem with racial tension: America had a problem with racism.

I wondered if America would ever have an African-American president and importantly, if he or she could ever change the racist attitudes that exist there. Perhaps, then, America would be the greatest nation on Earth?

35

Sometimes I did not appreciate how massive America actually is: North Carolina is of a similar size to England and some of the other forty-nine states are much larger. It was no surprise that around seventy per cent of America's population did not possess passports: there was so much to see there, and the horizon seemed unreachable.

I remembered going into my local bank in Rochdale to sort out my new mortgage, and as I waited, another member of staff started talking to me. Bear in mind that the school I was working in was just ten miles away from my home, at the time.

'Where do you work, luv?' she said.

'Near Manchester', I replied. She looked young enough to be my daughter!

'Oh, that's far, int it! I wun't like to travel that far', she commented in a very strong regional accent.

Obviously, each to their own, but would she drive sixty miles every day across North Carolina to get to and from work? I don't think she would. I don't think many people would! Maybe, the British have a smaller sense of scale because everything is within easier reach in comparison to much larger countries.

I had made a new online 'cyber-friend' named Clint who lived in Iowa and who had emailed me several times. Maybe he was a complete loner or had no friends outside of his own town but we seemed to 'get on' via email and he understood sarcasm! I had provisionally arranged to meet him in DC some time ago and I just hoped he was not an axe-murderer!

We did eventually talk once on the phone, and he seemed quite genuine, held an intellectual conversation and was polite. So, there are interesting people out there – even if they are 1,107 miles away! That is a sixteen-hour drive and not a twenty-minute drive to Manchester! He must have been desperate for company, or maybe he was an axe-murderer after all? We never did meet and I think he lived just a bit too far away to meet for a coffee!

I was concerned about how much weight I had gained. My waistline had expanded, my face was slowly filling out and I heard the expression 'You're looking well!' too many times.

The other day, I was talking to one of my students (who was Mexican) about Taco Bell and, as I patted my stomach mid conversation, she commented, 'You're ged-ding f-yat!', and I wondered what I would look like ten years down the line if I remained living in North Carolina.

Exercise had not been a priority and the only walking I was doing was to and from my car and, of course, roaming the mile-long aisles of Walmart. I was also eating out nearly every day. I generally felt more sluggish and seemed to get out of breath easily, which happened one day when I ran to my car in the pouring rain. I have always been a slim-Jim, so being chunkier felt strange, but after my student's comment, I felt it was time to get my lazier and fatter ass into gear, prompting me to get back to the gym the next day as my passion for weight training or any physical activity was waning.

My local gym was just a ten-minute drive from my apartment, so I had no excuses. I could not walk there without the risk of death by car trying to cross the US 70. I had strangely adapted to North Carolinian life in the very short time I had been there and nobody walked around – anywhere! It was strange at first but now I was at the point when I no longer noticed. If I did have to walk anywhere, it conjured up peculiar feelings of vulnerability. Once, when I walked from my apartment to the pool on the same complex, I even worried about a flock of aggressive blackbirds swooping down from the skies trying to peck my eyes out, similar to the Alfred Hitchcock film, *The Birds*. The only other time in my life when I felt vulnerable was during a safari on my first visit to South Africa with Phil. I asked my driver if I could step out of the jeep just for a few seconds, just long enough to feel what it must be like to be the prey of a lion; I was food and no longer a person. I can't believe to this day that I did that or that the driver even allowed me to, but it was a feeling of total vulnerability which was strangely exhilarating, making me feel completely and utterly aware of how powerless I was up against a man-eating lion. It must have been all the adrenaline in my body, an instinctive 'fight or flight' situation – an experience I will never forget.

Walking around North Carolina and the openness of the streets in Raleigh was in some ways similar, just because it had become unusual to walk, and in some ways psychologically disturbing. Maybe I had developed mild agoraphobia.

During a staff meeting that day, some of the teachers in my hall asked me what British kids did during the break time.

'Most of them go outside', I stated.

'Outsaade?'

'Yeah.'

'Isn't th-a-yt dangerous?'

'Dangerous?'

'Yeah, they might get nabbed or something.'

'No, they just go into the playground.'

'Really?'

'Yes. They go outside at lunchtime too, especially if it is dry weather. We encourage them to go out and get fresh air. In fact, some schools I have taught in don't like kids being inside at break time or lunch time.'

'Really?'

'Yeah, seriously!'

'Maybe we should traal th-ayt here', one of them said.

'Maybe you should. They might like it', I suggested.

That afternoon, my proposal was put forward to the vice-principal for discussion and the following day, the outside break trial began.

When the bell rang for the end of first block, the kids started walking into the hall and suddenly all the teachers started shouting, telling them to go outside in the sunshine, and I helped to usher them outside through the fire doors.

Many of them looked confused and thought there was a fire as they walked outside and looked scared. Some of them walked tentatively on the grass or looking down as if they were walking on it for the first time, looking around like frightened rabbits. One girl walked with her arms wrapped around her torso as if she had never been outside before as she said, 'I feel weird!' Many of them gravitated towards the fire doors and some others carried on walking around like a scene out of the *Stepford Wives*. Maybe they had agoraphobia, too – brought on from early childhood. I just thought they would be happy to be outdoors in the fresh air.

That evening, in the gym, following an initial assessment by a trainer, who looked more like a bulldozer and probably had less brains than one, asked me what my aims were. My reply: 'to have muscles kind of like yours?' He looked flattered but did not say much.

He quickly weighed me and jotted down a new training regime. I was surprised he could write yet disappointed I had only gained eight pounds. My belly seemed to have suddenly 'appeared' over the last few days. Maybe, too much fast food or spending too much time behind the wheel or both at the same time! Those drive-through's have a lot to answer for!

They did have a drive-through pharmacy and banks too, and at times, I thought a pickup truck, with an American flag etched on the back window and a pair of cow horns attached to its bonnet would have been more fitting and I could have driven off into the sunset, stopping at Bojangles' on the way.

I did have a conversation with a student in my new class about driving, who was sixteen and was excited about his impending driving lessons and he seemed too young to be driving.

'So, what car do you want?' I asked.

'My Da-y-d is goin' to baa me a pickup, so we can go huntin' together at the week-ey-nds.'

'Hunting, for what?'

'Bears and deer.'

'You shoot them?'

'Of course, and we go fishin' too. Aah can't wait to ge-y-t my truck.'

'Cool', I politely smiled as he seemed excited about his future adventures.

'Ahh wanna ge-y-t the American flag etched on maa back window with the words, America is great', I would love to see the reaction if I had 'Britain is great' etched on my back window in England. I would probably wake up to a burnt-out car with BNP painted all over its charred remains and complaints in the local newspapers.

The year was moving on quickly and I was beginning to feel strangely homesick. I was feeling like my old self again - content and confident. I never thought I would feel this way again and I wanted my American life to last as long as possible. Time and space really are healers, though at one point it was difficult to believe people when they said those words, even when they cared.

My state of mind made me think more sensibly about returning to England and how important family, friends and my country were to me. I knew my dad had been worried about me living in America and I thought it would be nice to live with him again, just for a short while until I sorted myself out before returning to London. Spending quality time with him would be good for me, and it would be nice for my dad too. He had been my source of strength over the last year, and will always be, and I wanted to make his life richer. Or if I did return to London, I could invite him down more often to broaden his mind and his world. I thought about my mum also and wanted to see more of her, as well as my auntie and my friends.

My decisions gave me nothing but warm and happy feelings – anxiety had evaporated. I was looking forward to my future: something that the break-up with Nick had stolen from me.

I returned to my apartment to face, yet another, pile of grading but managed to plough through it while watching Simon Cowell on TV. He really worked his British accent even more than in the UK, appearing more ruthless than ever on *American Idol*, although the Americans loved it. He always seemed to make the contestants cry and was hilarious to watch.

I have been guilty myself of over-exaggerating my accent to gain attention in order to boost my confidence even more but the way Americans were so interested was sometimes overwhelming yet I quite liked it, and it was refreshing. From my experience, British people are more reserved. Yesterday evening in Walmart, someone behind me overheard my conversation with the woman at the checkout as I paid for my groceries.

'You're Brid-ish!' she yelled excitedly. Her shopping trolley contained an ample supply of doughnuts and I really wanted to reply 'You're American!' in an equally excited manner.

'Yes I am.'

'We were sorry to hear about your Prince-yss Di-aana! Did yew ever meet her?' Well for a start, she was not *my* Princess Diana! Americans think we must randomly bump into royalty all the time while out shopping or have open invitations for tea at Buckingham Palace!

'No, I saw her once from a distance when she attended the premier of *Jurassic Park*.'

'We all loved her here. It's such a shame about her, she was so beaud-iful!' Would it have made any difference if she had not been beautiful? I had seen on the news how Americans were obsessed with her. Before she came on the scene fewer people in America paid attention to the Royals or could tell you the name of the Queen of England! I think Diana changed that, she was everyone's fairy-tale princess. Generally, people all around the world liked her, not just her beauty and kindness, but also her insecurities and visible emotions, which made her more likeable and more approachable.

Throughout history, people have always looked up to iconic women that have experienced tragedy in their lives: Boudicca, Joan of Arc, Emmeline Pankhurst, Ann Frank, Eva Peron, Mother Theresa, Marilyn Monroe and Jackie Kennedy. Maybe, Diana was a modern-day iconic tragic heroine to many people.

I had read somewhere that millions of people around the world go to England every year for one reason: they flock around Buckingham Palace to get a glimpse of the Royal Family. I have stood at its gates many times and the accents of the crowds were mainly American. The Royal Family does arguably generate a great deal of tourism. I am sure the British would prefer to see Disneyland rather than the Whitehouse (and I have been guilty of that too), although depending on who the future president is, maybe that would change, one day.

'Do yew thi-ynk it was really an accident?'

'I think it was just a tragic accident, that's all. Anyway, it is getting late. I'm sorry, I don't mean to be rude but I have to get home. It was nice to meet you though.'

It was actually nice to meet her and she seemed to be a genuinely pleasant person but I was feeling tired.

'That's no problem. It was naace to meet yew too. Yew have a great evening!' she smiled brightly.

'You too, goodbye.'

As I walked out of the main entrance, I noticed a hairdresser that was still open within 'Walmart world'. Do Americans ever stop working? I caught a reflection of myself and thought I was looking more like *Worzel Gummidge*, and despite feeling tired, I took my chances and went inside. There was one woman cutting hair, talking to another stylist.

'Hi, do I have to make an appointment?' I asked.

A woman around twenty years of age replied, in broad Southern drawl, 'No, yew can get a hair-cut now, if yew w-y-ant?'

'Would that be alright?'

'Sure.' I sat down as she placed a cape around my shoulders and started combing my hair.

'How was yer draave?' she asked.

'It was okay. I am just a bit tired.'

'Me too, you're gonna be maa last client! I'm buushed.'

'I know the feeling.' I smiled as I sighed at her in the reflection of the huge wall mirror.

'I'm Shana.'

'Hi, I'm Paul.'

'Pleased to meet yew!' She smiled at my reflection.

'Thanks for cutting my hair without an appointment.'

'That's faane. It happens all the taame, don't worry.'

'Are you part of Walmart?' I asked.

'Oh no, we are a sepa-rate b-uy-siness. Where are yew from, I don't recognise you accent?'

'I'm from England.'

'Oh...that must have been a long draave!'

'I meant, I am from the UK.'

'That's sti-y-ll a long draave! So, how do yew want it cuttin?'

I tried to remain phlegmatic, as I responded to her questions about my haircut.

'Just a bit shorter, please.' I stared at myself in the mirror, trying not to look too confused, while watching her comb through my hair and thinking about what she had just said. She still thought I had driven from England.

'Ah... you think I drove from New England?' I did not want to insult what intelligence she had.

'I meant, England, as in Britain, I'm British.'

'Yew are Bri-dish?' We talked to each other's reflections.

'Yes.'

She started finely cutting my hair with a small pair of scissors and then stopped, holding the scissors mid-air and stared at me with a blank expression, blinking once or twice. Her mouth slowly opened wider as if she was about to have a pre-molar filling extraction, but she then covered it with her hand and scissors before laughing. The laughter grew louder and louder, suddenly transforming into what can only be described as a strange hen-like-sound – a hen laying an abnormally large egg. 'CLUCKAAAAAWWWWK! Hey Tal-eena! I thought he was from New Ing-land. He's BRI-DISH!'

Suddenly, Taleena stopped in her tracks and started cackling too but her laughter changed into a 'hee-haw' sound. Taleena had also transformed, into a donkey!

If anyone should have been laughing hysterically, it should have been me: apparently, I had driven all the way from England to witness farmyard impressions in North Carolina. Part of me wanted to fill the sink in front of me with water and stick my head inside it, yet part of me wanted to break into song and sing, 'Old MacDonald had a farm'. I looked up with a bemused expression as they 'clucked' and 'hee-hawed'. Maybe I should have got out of my chair, put my hands under my armpits, head bucking backwards and forwards doing chicken impressions, squawking and running across the salon. I could not stop myself from giggling through the entire hair-cutting experience while trying to fathom whether the girls were truly 'rednecks', mentally challenged or just really fucking bored.

I left the salon having witnessed the theory of evolution in just thirty minutes.

36

April 2004

I was back at school feeling disgruntled, following the too-short four-day Spring Break – America's equivalent of a British two-week Easter holiday that I had been deprived of and still felt disgruntled about! I was surprised Easter was shorter here. We were only off school on Good Friday and Easter Monday, and then two more days, as we lost two other days due to the snow days we had accumulated during the winter months. We definitely need a lot more snow in England!

Disappointingly, I did not feel rested.

After weeks of thought, I finally made the decision to return to England. School was going to be finished in just over a month and then I wanted to spend some time in DC before I returned home. I contacted VIF, who deferred my flight home giving me extra time in America, which I appreciated.

I told the principal of my decision. Teaching math had been tougher than I thought and was a subject I never really enjoyed. I never had a passion for it at school, despite having a good maths teacher, and I certainly had not developed a passion for it as a teacher, although there were some activities I enjoyed doing with the kids such as making Halloween cards with mathematical questions inside. That was the creative side of me and I just had a mental block when it came to maths and had to go over it several times before it finally clicked, so maybe the school would have not kept me on teaching maths, after all. The subject had a 'fear-factor', however, I was grateful to Hayley for teaching me to appreciate maths more.

On reflection, I wish I had become an art teacher and not a science teacher. I fell in with a science- crowd at school and the rest is history (even though, my biology teacher at secondary school was inspiring). I never really had been a source of scientific knowledge and when people ever asked me questions relating to science, either I didn't reply or I didn't answer them as a scientist would and that sometimes

211

rattled me. I just liked science but I was never really a walking talking encyclopaedia.

Over the Spring Break, I did a lot of relaxing in DC. I have always had a diverse taste in films and I watched *Passion of the Christ*, although it was not for the faint-hearted. It lacked many of the special effects we are often bombarded with but more importantly, the acting was very good, especially by Jim Caviezel: uncomfortable yet compelling to watch. Some scenes were brutal, causing many people in the audience to look away, especially when Christ was beaten.

I also watched *Eternal Sunshine of the Spotless Mind* with Jim Carey and Kate Winslet. I never really rated them as reputable actors until I watched this film as it was excellent. It is about falling in love, being hurt and then going to get treatment to erase your memory of the person who broke your heart! If only that was possible - events in our lives happen for a reason.

It rained for most of the time in DC. The weather in the south-eastern United States is more extreme than in the UK. When it rained in North Carolina, it was monsoon season and when it was hot, it was as humid as a tropical rainforest; sometimes, it was better to take a spare shirt out with you as you could be soaked within ten minutes. I sweat sometimes when it is cold but could never imagine life there without air-conditioning. Almost every building I had been in – school classrooms, a public library, art galleries, museums, restaurants – had it, and I could not have driven my car without the air conditioning being switched on.

People have said that DC used to be swampland but the city just happens to be near lots of river basins. The one name that grabbed my attention was the Potomac River which is just over 400 miles long, making it the fourth largest river along the Atlantic coast of the United States and the twenty-first largest in the United States. Over 5 million people live within the Potomac watershed.

Logically speaking, how could any city be built on a swamp? Surely, it would sink? Today, however, was a pleasant 75 degrees Fahrenheit. The only thing missing was a swamp!

Glen and I walked to the mall between the Washington Monument and the Capitol Building and walked on further to the Tidal Basin. The Potomac River swells at that time of the year because of all the precipitation (they did not to call it rain). The Tidal Basin was, incidentally, surrounded by cherry trees in blossom.

'I like these cherry trees?' I stated.

'They were a gift from Mayor Yukio Ozaki of Tokyo City', he replied. 'I am full of random facts, aren't I? Apparently, it looks like a pink circle if you fly over it from Reagan Airport, especially when they are in full bloom.'

'I'd like to see that.'

Reagan Airport is in Central DC. From the Tidal Basin, we could clearly see the neoclassical style Jefferson Memorial, which looked elegant and is quite a sight. We walked up the steps of the memorial to see the majestic bronze statue of Jefferson. The views from the steps were just spectacular. It was amazing just ambling around the city all day with nothing to worry about.

We were hungry, so we walked around to find food. Glen knew of a good restaurant, it was a Peruvian chain called Granja De Oro (this means 'Golden Farm'). I ate half a Peruvian roast chicken and it was the best chicken I had ever tasted.

The following day, we ate at an Ethiopian restaurant, using our fingers. It felt ethnic sharing the same food served in a round silver bowl with a spongy flatbread called 'injera' – it was the national dish in Ethiopia and Eritrea.

We later watched *Bowling for Columbine* on DVD, which I wanted to buy when I returned to England. I was not sure if this film had been released back home yet but it was about gun culture in America. The school where twelve students were shot was in the same area that the cartoon *Southpark* was based on. The two students apparently went bowling before they went into the school and shot innocent kids.

Later that evening, we visited the Lincoln Memorial. I really wanted to see this, in some ways due to the film *Planet of the Apes*, when Mark Walberg crashes his space ship on the steps of the memorial. He then walks into the memorial only to see a huge statue of an ape. Importantly, the statue of President Lincoln was equally colossal.

How did people build these gigantic statues and memorials without the use of modern machinery and sculpt them so perfectly? DC is full of memorials and statues and the ones I saw were all equally impressive: the Vietnam Memorial, the Korean Memorial and I liked the Einstein Statue.

Although Clayton and the surrounding areas were scenic and tranquil, with cotton fields and cornfields dominating the unlimited open space, I was hungry for culture and as we walked down to the Smithsonian Institute, I wanted to go into every museum and art gallery – we were definitely, spoilt for choice.

'Most of the museums are free to enter', Glen pointed out.

In fact, the Smithsonian's 30 million annual visitors are admitted without charge. We walked past the Washington Monument which looked more like a giant sharpened pencil, but I could not help noticing how dignified it looked, and, despite its height, it was not overpowering.

'I think you will enjoy the Holocaust Museum although I am not sure if 'enjoy' is the correct word to use.'

'I have heard about it. I would like to see it but I don't know if we will have enough time as it's getting late now', I replied.

However, Glen wanted me to see it, and as we entered, we were given a card each (in the form of a small booklet) telling the story of a real person who lived or died during the Holocaust. Mine was about David J. Selznik, born in Lithuania in 1912. The card explained his background, his capture and he described the horrors he witnessed of Jewish children being taken to the top floor of a building and dropped out of windows and left to die in the street below. It made me think of how horrible people could be to each other just because they are of a different race or religion.

David J. Selznik was one of the lucky ones: he escaped from a ghetto and immigrated to the United States in 1949.

I looked at Glen and said, 'I will always keep this.'

A small smile appeared on his sorrowful face, before he spoke. 'It makes me sad, especially because I have Jewish friends.'

A sign in the museum explained a 'ghetto' is an area of a city, especially a very poor area, where people of a particular race or religion live closely together and were separated from other people. The Nazis revived the medieval term to describe their system of concentration and control, the compulsory Jewish Quarter. Sadly, most Jews were forced to live in these ghettos.

The museum was absorbing yet sombre, a place for reflection and remembrance. A few exhibits caught my attention, especially one of a metal case with twenty glass eyes fixed inside it. Each eye was a different shade of blue or green and I had never realised there was so many different shades. This metal case would have been held up against a Jewish person's face to compare eye colour and if it did not match one of the glass eyes, that person would have been exterminated. Glen and I did not speak much, I think we were both deep in thought and felt saddened by everything as we looked around.

There was also a pole with strands of human hair on it of various colours of blonde and auburn and, again, if the colour did not match, the Jewish person was exterminated. The Nazi's blended antisemitism with science. One of the signs read: '*Nazism* is applied biology' – this was stated by Rudolf Hess (Adolf Hitler's deputy). More ominously, the Nazi authorities worked to rid themselves of the expense of keeping alive people who were mentally and physically disabled, whom they called 'life unworthy of life' and there were small gas chambers with life-like dummies of mentally and physically handicapped children inside them. It's chilling how people with birth defects or brown eyes were considered to be of 'no use'. These weren't just 'exhibits' but evidence of the atrocities that really happened.

It was exactly a four-hour drive back to Clayton, and all I could think of on my journey was the Holocaust Museum and how deeply moved I was by my visit. Although everyone has heard of the Holocaust, seeing those exhibits and reading all the information, the torture methods and the numbers killed, made me fully appreciate what these people went through and it was a reminder of how we should treat each other, regardless of race, colour, religion or sexual orientation.

When I arrived home, there was a letter waiting for me in my post box: my return flight tickets to England had arrived. My American journey would soon be over.

37

May 2004

Another busy month at school had passed quickly and the weather was improving. Glen decided to come down and visit that weekend, even though I had not planned very much. He seemed more interested in me and I was beginning to let my guard down, growing fond of him too.

Glen was shorter, had lost most of his hair despite being 28 years old. He had bright blue eyes and white teeth – in fact, all Americans had great teeth! He always remained calm and was quietly spoken. He had a certain enigma: reflective, calming, organised yet impulsive, modest and tenderly spoken. Despite living alone, he had a busy life, was not career orientated but brimmed with intelligent subject matter.

On the Saturday, the weather was unusually warm, so we spontaneously decided to drive down the US 70 to Atlantic beach.

The weather already felt humid, despite being May. Atlantic Beach is located on the eastern portion of the Bogue Banks (a barrier island on the Atlantic coast) and the town is bordered to the south by the Atlantic Ocean and to the north by Bogue Sound, part of North Carolina's Crystal Coast.

Glen said he had heard of a place called Emerald Isle, but to get there meant driving down the length of the Bogue Banks. We wanted to spend some time on the beach first, walk around, grab an ice cream and just relax. I wanted to make the most of this weekend and the weather before the EOGs started at school.

After parking the car, we walked towards the beach, dressed in shorts, vests and flip-flops. It was quiet, despite it being lunch time. We walked silently through the sandy car park towards two big pickup trucks parked parallel to each other.

Leaning against each pickup were two women of similar age, height and build. They must have been in their early thirties, tall and weighing in at twenty stone each. Both were dressed in over-sized dark shorts, baggy T-shirts and they donned baseball caps. Everything about them seemed super-sized: their cars, the half-empty two-litre coke bottles, their bodies and clothing, their tyres, their hands and they had the loudest voices – literally shouting at each other despite the short distance between them. We thought they were arguing, but as we approached, we could hear they were in mid conversation.

'BOBBI HA-YD THE BEST TAAME OF HER LAAFE!'
'OH, YEAH, WHAT DID SHE GE-YT FOR HER BIRTHDAY?'
'SHE GOT THREE PLAY-MOBILES, AHH, SHE LOVED EM!'
'OH YEAH, THOSE ARE REAL CUTE!'

Their voices were truly deafening.

'Welcome to America!' Glen uttered discreetly and sarcastically, as we neared the car park exit that lead to the desolate sandy beach.

'Thank you', I grinned sheepishly.

'You know something, they had no awareness of how loud they were talking.'

'I haven't got the faintest clue why not.'

Despite the wind blowing quite fiercely off the ocean, we could still hear them talking about 'Bobbi's par-dy'.

'Why are they not aware of how loud they talk?' I asked.

'I think many Americans don't have the shame gene.'

'What do you mean?'

'I think a lot of Americans are not ashamed of themselves. That's what I mean.'

'Why do you say that?'

'I read it somewhere, that shame and guilt are negative self-conscious emotions, experienced in situations of failure.'

'Americans don't like failure, do they?'

'No. It's in our culture.'

'Maybe it's a combination of genetics and the environment', I added.

'It's hard to explain why, but living in America myself and not being fully American, I can think it's mainly the way you are brought up and what is expected of you. I kind of have it inbuilt and see it every day at work, even though I am half Peruvian. We are brought

218

up like that as children, to be competitive, to be confident and put yourself first, and I think it stays with you.'

I remembered back to when I was travelling as a student in the USA; I overheard a conversation between two businessmen standing near my seat on a train to Manhattan who openly discussed their salaries on the full carriage.

'I am on fifty kay now and I wanna be on sixty next year. What about you?'

The other guy responded just as openly, and I think he received a higher salary, as if he was in direct competition. Everyone around me on the carriage could hear what I thought should have been a private conversation between two people. I certainly wouldn't openly disclose my pay in front of strangers. They either didn't seem to care who heard, were boasting or were completely unaware of anyone else's presence. I still remembered that conversation from fourteen years ago because it just seemed 'different'.

I suddenly thought about the old American woman in the library. She had an air of confidence about her and she was direct yet polite. I also thought about the girl I taught: Louna, one of the 'quieter' students, although, she was slightly more hesitant about speaking, she still had an air of confidence.

'Maybe it is about nurturing and the impact of the environment you grow up in. I have taught children in Northern England who seemed more reserved than children in London, even when the northern children were more intelligent. Maybe southern British people feel more insecure and that's why they come across more confident. I wonder if this theory applies to the differences between Americans and British, although maybe there are other factors?'

'Such as?'

'Maybe the size of your country influences everything you do. Here you have to be bigger and bolder, and maybe that has an influence on your psyche too. Your car and my car are big by British standards. You are on your own most of the time, and if you lived in England, you would probably own a small hatchback.'

'Maybe, you're right.'

'Maybe it has also got something to do with history and culture.'

'Do you think America lacks that?'

'You know what I mean, Glen. European history goes much further back than American history; I'm just thinking about the culture I experience when I visit most European countries.'

I suddenly pictured the littered Roman ruins on the streets of Rome and thought about how quickly they built a very modern pharmacy opposite where I lived in Clayton, and the concrete food inlets off the US 70 and my modern American life that, even then, sometimes didn't feel real.

'I know what you are saying. Maybe some Americans feel insecure about that and make up for it with their character and their loudness. Is that how people see us?'

'I can't speak for everyone and it's not fair to stereotype, but many people abroad think Americans are louder and overenthusiastic.'

'Maybe we are!'

'But I have met some genuinely nice people in North Carolina, who seem humble and are the kindest of people. I will be honest, when I was in DC at that Jewish dinner you took me to, I felt out of my depth'.

'In what way?'

'I don't know, I just...didn't feel clever enough or something. They seemed to know a lot and were interested in everything. They asked me who my local MP was, and I did not know things about England that they knew. They asked about my ancestry, where my grandparents were from. People don't tend to ask that back in England. I thought they were all intelligent and I felt a bit stupid, in comparison, if I'm honest.'

'Did you feel uncomfortable?'

'Yes and no. I guess I just felt ... different.'

'Well, you are intelligent. You know a lot about biology.'

'Maybe, but I don't know a lot about life, sometimes. I guess that's just me.'

'Everybody liked you!' Glen then gently put his arm around my shoulders and smiled at me. Maybe he detected I felt isolated and a bit different from everyone around me. I felt 'foreign' and it was sometimes not a good feeling.

'Maybe I would feel the same in your shoes,' he added.

'One expression does annoy me though.'

'What's that then?'

'Americans overuse the word awesome.'

'Awesome!' I laughed as Glen truly exaggerated the word in an American accent.

'I would only use that word if I was in a space ship looking down on planet Earth. Now that would be awesome!' I smirked.

'I know; we are all idiots.'

We had been on Atlantic beach for some time so we decided to drive on to Emerald Isle and down the lengths of Bogue Banks.

The road was flat and you could see the Atlantic Ocean on one side for most of the journey and then on both sides as the bank narrowed.

We arrived at a street near Emerald Isle where the houses were identical - all were tall and the gardens had perfectly manicured lawns with large circular wooden flower pots at the start of the drives. Everything was perfectly neat and there was an American flag on a large pole waving in the wind half-way down the avenue. Was this the American dream or an American dream world? In reality, it was an American tropical paradise with million-dollar homes built everywhere.

It had been a nice day. The air was beginning to cool and we decided to stop for a burger on the way back to Clayton. It was enjoyable to be driven and I dozed off for some of the journey back home.

I was not looking forward to going back to school and I did not want this weekend, of all weekends, to end.

38

The year seemed to have flown by, yet I had learnt a lot about North Carolina. I warmed quickly to culture here, the people I had met, the places I had visited, situations I had been involved in and had learned some differences and similarities between the UK and the US. Importantly, I had the space and time to reflect on myself.

At school, it was hard to believe the students were about to take their EOG's. After all the build-up, it was a strange feeling, and despite finally finding my feet and adapting to life, I suddenly realised my time was limited as soon, my American adventure would end.

The EOG's had multiple-choice questions and I was not too clear if they were easier or more difficult but there is definitely less writing to do, for sure, and I know how the students hated copying off the white board. Some answers seemed too obvious but the maths paper still required students to work out problems out for themselves. Hayley had been teaching booster revision classes to combined maths groups so they were fully prepared for the maths EOG - she was the expert. The Language Arts EOG involved a written passage reading, as they did in English examinations, yet still, the questions were multiple choice.

On the day the EOG's started, a teaching assistant burst into my classroom, gaily skipped around, waving a plastic magic wand, gently tapping each student on the head wishing them luck. In some ways, this surprised me, as I thought the idea of magic in this part of the States would not have gone down well, especially as people living in the Bible Belt were opposed to any form of magic or spells and Harry Potter was off the curriculum.

I had lost count the number of times I had heard people say, 'God bless.' One of the students who went hunting with his dad also told me that on his sixteenth birthday, his dad was going to buy him a pick-up truck with the words 'God bless America' etched on his rear window and that still resonated in my mind.

I had seen many over-sized pick-up trucks driving around with 'America is the greatest' etched on their rear windows on a daily basis. Make America Great Again', was a campaign slogan used in American politics that originated during the *Ronald Reagan* campaign in 1980. I wondered why we don't have that essence of patriotism in British culture today. In Britain, the only patriotic types of cars I have seen were 1970's minis with Union Jacks painted on their roofs. Generally, the British just seem to 'get on with it'. I never have viewed Britain as being the Greatest or England for that matter, despite it being called Great Britain. I have sometimes viewed London as being a 'great city' but not a 'Great City' and having supremacy over other cities in England. I think being outside in the open-air walking on the Pennines, is a great feeling but not 'Great'. I have never considered my country as being 'Great' in a way, that is superior to the rest of the world, but it seems that it is another inherent feeling amongst its people - America is the greatest nation which, resonates around the world.

I looked at the teaching assistant again tapping the last student on the head with her magic wand; waving the wand was just meaningless fun and nothing more. This magic wish made students laugh and eased their nerves.

I thought about the spells I did. They had meaning but were not funny, they brought me nothing but false hope and misery.

The students wrote answers on a 'bubble sheet' using a pencil dot in the correct answer: A, B, C or D. These answer sheets are later 'fed' through a machine which marks them in seconds. Back in the UK, examiners are employed and paid little doing arduous hours of marking and the one year I did it, I recall it being a painful and ungratifying process.

The students have three tests: Math (non-calculator), Math (calculator) and Reading. The average level is 3, which most students achieve, although some do obtain level 4. I found out later, some of my math students achieved level 4, which was pleasing, to say I have never taught maths before, although Hayley did help me with their revision!

On Thursday, after school, all the teachers assembled in the dining hall, to 'bubble' in the sheets – just making sure, they were all perfectly completed, before posting. Each teacher also had to bubble in the correct codes for their classes and work with another teacher, which took around one hour to complete.

The following day, the school counsellor collected the bubble sheets and took them to the District office - all done under 'high security'. At the District Office, they were fed through a *Scanotron* Machine and the students obtained their results the same day - a very efficient process, unlike in the UK, where students wait until mid-August for their results, proving more differences and similarities between the USA's and the UK's education system.

It was a relaxing way to end what had been a busy week, as on Friday, cleverly planned into the school calendar, was Sports Day! Here, this event is titled - 'Field Day'.

Just like all British schools I have worked in, Sports Day is right at the end of the school year, although more often than not, it rains and turns out to be the chilliest day of the summer with kids sat around complaining and shivering.

Today, however, was the epitome of glorious North Carolinian sunshine and it looked beautiful.

Smells of hotdogs, doughnuts and candyfloss filled the air and all the kids dressed even more casually, and most wore baseball caps, including myself – the scene around me looked typically American.

There were no track races, no hurdles or discus, in fact not a sporting event in sight. As I took a break from my stall, I looked around some of the other events: Egg and Spoon Race, Tug-O-War and I was responsible for running the Apple Dunking stall.

Everyone looked happy and relaxed, even the teachers were smiling and joking with the kids. I bought a bottle of Gatorade and quickly returned to my stall.

'Go on Mr Wood, do it!' The students beckoned me to stick my head in the bucket of water. Many of them started to join and shouted.

'MR WOOOOOD, MR WOOOOOOD, MR WOOOOOOOD!'

The pronunciation of Wood was longer and louder each time and they chanted, 'DOO IT, DOOO IT, DOOOO IT!' Everyone around me whooped and screamed excitedly.

I looked inside the bucket and there was more frothing saliva floating around in the water than pieces of apple.

'There's more diseases in there than a nurses handbook!' I uttered. An expression Robbie often used. Thankfully, nobody heard me, as everyone continued shouting. They just wanted to see me dunked. I removed my baseball cap, closed my eyes, hoped for the best and did it. I quickly pulled my head out of the bucket and luckily, there was a towel next to the bucket. I do not think even a dog (or a dawg) would have drank that water.

After doing high-fives with most of the kids, as they continued to cheer, I walked around the field, and as the sun blazed down, my dampened T-shirt and hair quickly dried.

Some teachers competed against the 8th-grade students in the Tug-O-War event but the teachers were no match against many of the stronger farm boys. There was also a bubble gum contest to see who could blow the biggest bubble; even the principle joined in! What happened to the 100 metre sprints here? There was also a twinky-eating contest (which raised my eyebrows), involving eating a small cake as quickly as possible and many people took part as it was a chance to eat free cake, and this seemed to be most popular attraction of the whole field day.

Other competitions included a water-balloon contest – many different coloured balloons filled with water randomly placed on the sports field, which students threw at each other, and more importantly, any teacher who dared to venture near them – and obviously, they did. After all, this was fun!

Five kids decided to chase me with the biggest bucket of water across the field, not realising how fast I could sprint. I even surprised myself! I thought about how much fun this was, so I deliberately slowed down as the sprinting kids caught up and drenched me. I think it made their day - their field day! Yet, this field day was no sporting contest: it was just an excuse to have mindless fun and it reminded me of the zany 1970's TV kid's programme - *The Banana Splits*.

After a fun-filled day, and now relaxing on the couch in the comfort of my apartment, I stared blankly watching TV, thinking about the Field Day, and how well I knew the kids and the teachers, in such a short space of time.

I thought about my 'American life' once again and looked around at the furniture in my apartment and soon, this would be an empty space again.

I thought about the security inside my car, the security I felt here, the lonely highways and all the driving, and how the roads would go on into an endless horizon. I remembered how many times I drove around getting lost and trying to find my way home, the long journeys and how many miles I had driven, getting lost deliberately, sometimes feeling lost in my mind whilst on the road; this journey, my personal journey, a journey to the remotest parts of North Carolina and the journeys to the loneliest parts of my mind.

My students would soon embark on their final journey of school life - High school - and would soon be grown up. This had not just been just another year of their lives; it had been an important year of their lives and mine.

39

Late May 2004

It was the last day at school and it felt sad to see these 8th-grade students leave school, and importantly, our lives.

All the teachers stood outside the front of the school and, as we waved, they boarded the yellow school buses or got into their parents' cars and drove away down the school drive.

I waved at Luke (the quiet one) who looked back and smiled and wondered what impact I had on his life. In years to come, he would be married with his own children and I am certain, one day he would turn out to be a good man and a great father.

As the last car drove away, the teachers slowly walked back inside the school. Our job and their job were over, although we had several more days left in school, called, teacher workdays. During this time, I filed everything away, pulled all the artefacts and photographs out of the glass cabinet and generally tidied the classroom. By the end of the day, everything was back to the way it was when I first walked through the classroom door, almost a year ago.

The following day, I drove into Micro as I wanted to buy a present for Hayley, and I bought her a flower from a small florist and made her a big card out of paper, writing her messages and drew lots of pictures of reminders of all the funny times we had and the situations I had been in. She really appreciated it and I would sincerely miss her. She was not just a work-colleague; she had become a dear friend.

After out last day in school, I said my goodbyes and thanked the principal, vice-principal and receptionist, and after school, all teachers from my hall went to a restaurant in Smithfield. As we laughed and joked and ate a cake they had bought me, I made a short speech thanking everyone for their support. They also gave me a card, which had been signed by everyone in the school, and after hugging the main teachers I had got to know well, particularly Hayley and Tee, we all went our separate ways – a strange feeling.

I arranged with VIF to stay another three weeks, giving me more time in DC. I made plans to sell my furniture and left the advert in the reception office at the apartment complex and, amazingly, the next day, it was all sold 'in promise' to a retired couple from Oklahoma.

I met them the following day and showed them around my apartment. They seemed rather eccentric and his wife started telling me about her brother who had recently been killed in a gas explosion. I had no idea what to say, except 'I'm sorry about your loss.'

They planned to have all the furniture including the TV moved out of my apartment in the next few days. Soon, I would be sleeping on the floor again on my last day in my apartment just as I did on my first day – I had come full circle.

Soon, I would be leaving North Carolina to stay with Glen until I returned to the UK. I still could not believe this year was almost over and it seemed my whole time here was school, hurdles and driving.

40

Early June 2004

I drove to Washington, DC, for the last time. I still enjoyed driving past cotton fields and the open empty space in North Carolina that seemed to go on forever. I would miss driving on the I-95, knowing the final destination was the Capital city of America.

The I-95 was an impressive route. I had researched it was the main Interstate Highway on the East Coast of the United States, running parallel to the Atlantic Ocean, and sometimes, I just wanted to drive on it forever.

Glen had once told me, 'sections of the Interstate are straight, so planes can land on them during emergencies.' I had noticed that every few miles, a section of the highway was indeed completely straight, so maybe it was true.

I liked seeing that familiar sign on the I-95, which read Petersberg 31 miles, Richmond 53 miles and Washington 161 miles: my journey broken down into bite-sized chunks. Even though I drove constantly for four hours at 60 mph – landmarks of my journey, each time.

This weekend was more low-key, but we visited the Corcoran Gallery of Art; they had an exhibition of Murial Hasbun photographs. I really enjoyed going on a paddleboat across the Tidal Basin, now devoid of that striking pink circle of trees.

It was now mid-summer and incredibly hot. I enjoyed the view over the lake and the reflections of trees in the water as I reflected on life too.

We paddled slowly in the midday heat and I looked up into the sky and a plane was flying so low, I could see its windows. It must have been landing at Reagan airport, several miles away. Reagan Airport was the national airport, whereas Dulles, another airport in Virginia, was 20 miles away from DC but was the international airport. There was another airport in Baltimore which was much further away.

I knew that I would be spending more time in DC alone during the day whilst Glen worked but I was looking forward to exploring the city. I had read somewhere that if you walk for half an hour a day, you can lose one pound in a week. Those future walks were going to be my workouts!

We were close to the *Washington Monument* and it reminded me of a gigantic obelisk, similar to one I had seen in Cairo a few years ago: tall, four-sided, narrow with a tapered ending in a pyramid shape at the top. This one was much taller, although it had no hieroglyphics written down the sides!

I think we were both deep in thought as we continued to paddle, slowly and effortlessly, across the Tidal Basin. It's still surface emphasised reflections of the iconic buildings around it: the *Washington Monument,* the *Jefferson Memorial*, the *Martin Luther King Memorial*, and the *Franklin Delano Roosevelt Memorial*.

I looked at Glen again. 'This is a special place and you are special to me, too.'

He smiled. 'Hey, you have experienced a lot during your time here.'

'It's all down to you. Thank you.'

'Maybe you can mention me when you write a book about it?'

I looked at him and smiled. 'Yes, maybe.'

There had been a slight shift of mood. I looked at him sat there looking humble: his bright blue eyes looking into the water and the deep expression in his face just as deep as the water.

'What do you wanna do next?' he suddenly asked.

'Can we stay here all day?'

'You might get hungry!' he joked.

After we finished paddling, we walked down the *Mall*, stopping at a festival with a lorry decorated in an Indian style, and then stopped for some food at a marketplace.

The bright blue sky in the heat of the day made everything look intense as the leaves shone and the Capitol Building ahead of us shimmered with clarity. I loved Washington, DC, especially in the summer and sometimes wished I could live here too, although I knew the remoteness and calmness of North Carolina had been the best place for me over the last year.

We walked back to Glen's car and drove on. 'There is something I want to show you.'

'Oh yeah?' He laughed.

We got out of the car and walked over to an ornate-looking building. 'It looks Greek', I added.

'It's the National Archives Building. It displays the Constitution, the Bill of Rights, and the Declaration of Independence'.

'You certainly know your facts, don't you? I hardly know anything about London and I lived there for eight years!'

'I am sure you know something about London. Paul, is there anywhere else you would like to see?'

'I'd really like to see John Kennedy's grave, if that's okay?'

'We will have to drive there, as it is in Virginia and it is a bit of a walk around up there. It's up to you?'

'I don't mind. I'd like to see it, as long as you don't mind driving again?'

'I think I have seen everything in this damned city three times over.' He laughed. 'Come on, let's go.'

'Sure.'

We drove to Arlington Cemetery and once we arrived, and after a quite a long walk, I stopped and bent down to look at the perfect lines of white headstones and took a photograph between two horizontal lines. Each headstone had the same shape, about one foot high with a slightly curved top. Some bore names yet some were marked unknown. All these people died in conflict – so much death around us and it was peaceful yet tragic on a huge scale knowing that so many people had died in wars. It seemed impossible to count the number of headstones just in one section.

As we walked on, we stopped to marvel at the view from Arlington House, overlooking Arlington Cemetery looking down a steep hill, which opened up to a wider view of the Lincoln Memorial - a beautifully white perfect squared building that stood out as a prominent feature. It's an awesome view eh?' I smiled as I listened to Glen remembering our past conversation.

'Yeah, it is actually awesome. Is that the Pentagon in the distance?'

'Indeed, it is.'

'This view does remind me of something.'

'What?'

'Something from my past.' I started to reminisce.

'Washington, DC?'

'It reminds me of a board game I used to play when I was a kid.'

'Which board game?'

'It was called, Game of Life.'

'What was the game about?'

'It was a game representing life and the good things and the bad things that happen to you. It was a big flat board with white buildings - houses, monuments, universities slotting into the board and straight roads connecting them all.'

'Did it have a wheel in the middle that twirled around?'

'Yes.' I laughed quietly as I continued to look ahead.

'I think we have all played that game.'

'The Game of Life?' I asked.

'Not the game. I mean life.'

'Life sometimes feels like a game that we all play.'

'Exactly.'

'This is no game, real life is right in front of us. You and I are living it, in fact, we all are living it, no matter where we are in the world or who we are.' Glen looked at me, as I looked back at him, confused about what I was saying.

As I looked back at the view, I had more flashbacks playing that game surrounded by the people I loved all those years ago – my brother, my dad, my cousin, my Auntie and Nana. I thought about the difficulties my brother and I faced as we grew up together, going through the challenges of school, the bullying, the happy memories and the hardships. Going through a difficult break up sparking the feelings of my parent's divorce, and my mother standing by the door wearing a fur coat with big hair wrapped in a headscarf with blue curlers at the front, the day my parents broke up, while we were young and the difficulties that presented of not having a mother in our early lives. My mind flashed forward to the present time.

I continued to look out at the horizon of Washington, DC, reflecting and comparing the view to what now, seemed a distant memory of playing that game with my family. I compared moving that green plastic car with a blue peg in the driving seat to driving my green car on the long and lonely roads in America and along the straight roads between the white iconic buildings in Washington, D.C. Stopping and starting with each spin of the wheel to turning the key in the ignition and travelling along the road of life.

Glen looked at me. 'Life is hard for many people.'

'I know.'

'You really loved him, didn't you?'

'Who?' Glen caught me off guard.

'Nick.'

I looked at Glen and smiled. 'Yes. That is now all in the past.' For a few precious minutes, I had forgotten.

We walked on for some time, silently, until we arrived at the Kennedy graves. The graved area was paved with irregular slabs of stone with what looked like clover growing out of the crevices giving it a somewhat, rustic appearance.

John F. Kennedy's circular headstone was made from Cape Cod granite, quarried near the site of the President's home and selected by members of his family. It had an eternal flame in the centre, which was mesmerizing, lit by Jackie Kennedy, who was later buried next to him and their children: tragedy within a family surrounded by the tragedies of wars.

41

Early July 2004

I was back in North Carolina for my final few days.

The weather had been exceptionally hot and I had spent most afternoons sunbathing by the pool after returning home from school. It felt like spending a summer holiday in Costa De La Sol. Although, one day after school, it rained so hard that I felt like I was aquaplaning in my car along the highway.

The seasons seemed different in North Carolina, as spring lasted a couple of weeks and then, it was full-on summer. Apparently, it also becomes unbearable in DC as it can sometimes reach 100 degrees Fahrenheit.

After another couple of hours sunbathing by the pool, I walked back to my apartment to relax. I switched on the TV to watch the news. It was announced that DC was to expect a swarm of Cicadas, as many as one million per acre, and they were supposed to cover trees and make a noise level, equivalent to a lawnmower. They are the world's longest living insect and hibernate underground emerging once every 17 years. How lucky was I to witness that? I think if that happened I might have shortened my stay in DC. Apparently, they do not bite and are 'stupid', as they fly into you but apparently, taste delicious to birds and dogs and some people even eat them!

It was my final day in North Carolina and the elderly couple who wanted to buy all my furniture and belongings knocked on the door around 10 a.m. I had spent the last few days packing everything mainly into plastic bags, and these and the furniture were loaded into their pick-up truck parked near the apartment block. Despite their age, they helped me to empty my apartment and load up the truck, although they were both breathing irratically! Once this was all done, we slowly drove away to their nearby home in Clayton, unloaded everything and they offered me freshly made lemonade and a cookie. It felt strange seeing and helping to lay out my old furniture in their new home.

They drove me back and I spent my last night at the apartment, sleeping on the deep pile carpet next to my luggage, just as I did on the first day I arrived.

Glen arrived around midday, the following day. Before I closed the door, I glanced quickly at an empty apartment that was full of memories and smiled before locking the door for the last time. We drove separately, to give my car back to the leasing company. It was sad to say goodbye to something that had given me independence and allowed me to see so much even though it was only a tiny part of America and without that car, I may never have met Glen. We then drove back to the complex in Glen's car to hand the keys back to Hayley. I hugged her and we exchanged email addresses. We stopped for a late lunch at Nando's before driving back to Washington, DC, unloaded three suitcases, ate dinner and quickly fell asleep.

After spending three wonderful weeks in DC, living in Glen's apartment, which now felt like a second home, my last day, however, had finally arrived.

I knew that I was loved here, in the USA, even though for a short time. One man who befriended and fell in love with me was Glen and saying 'goodbye' to him and everything here would be difficult because I had grown to love him. Without this man, I would have found it harder to live there and heal in North Carolina and he showed me Washington, DC – another world.

It was 7 August 2004, and I was in the capital city of the USA and it was raining heavily. Glen got out of bed and looked through the window at the rain for several seconds.

'Look, even Washington is sad that you are leaving.'

As I relaxed on the bed, waking up, I looked up at him. I could see the tears welling up in his eyes. I looked at him, and a tear ran down my face. He lay down next to me.

'I don't want to leave you alone here', I said quietly.

'I'll be fine.'

'I just hope the memories don't come back when I return to England.'

'I don't think they will.' He spoke softly with confident reassurance. 'You are stronger now.'

I composed myself quickly. He had been a good friend as well as my American boyfriend. I felt uplifted as he calmed me down.

I was aware of the fears I had before, but it felt different now. There was no pain. I also knew that this new relationship would end too, in just a matter of hours.

'You are right. I am happy. Really, I am. I am sad too. I am sad to leave you here, alone. I hate the thought of you being here on your own. Even when you have been at work, I have liked it here, in your home. I have really enjoyed the last three weeks here and it feels like this has been the final part of my healing. Thank you for everything.'

'You are always welcome back here'. Glen was trying to reassure me. 'I am sure you will come back again, one day.' He spoke kindly.

'Being here feels like ...'

'Home?'

'Yes.'

'I know.'

'It seems unfair that I have to leave you now, just when I am feeling this happy. There are so many things that I want to do with you, here in DC.'

'I think we have done everything here.' We both laughed.

'You know what I mean. Life is now moving on, and you are part of it.'

I knew then, at that moment, that this was the boost I needed in order to face what lay ahead of me. I was feeling happy and positive about returning to the UK.

It was nearly 10.30 am, and we had to be at the airport in 3 hours. We had talked for over an hour, although at times, it felt intense, it was actually a release, to let go of some emotions. We had our breakfast, cereal, followed by toast, with Strawberry jam and Brie cheese.

'This feels very French doesn't it? Are you not supposed to eat Brie cheese with Cranberry jelly?' I asked, intuitively.

'Well, the French eat cheese and jam together, don't they? Do you

236

like it?' Glen expertly and confidently explained.

'I love it. It is an interesting combination; they complement each other.' Glen looked at me and smiled.

As we ate breakfast, the atmosphere between us became less intense, and I was feeling at peace. We finished our breakfast and Glen remained quiet. He was dreading this day, probably more than I was. The atmosphere had been charged with emotions and I began to feel anxious with a heavy feeling inside my heart. I tried to convince myself that everything would be okay and starting a new life back in the UK would be a new chapter.

'Just look at this apartment. I love it!' I said, excitedly.

I had his moved furniture around for him whilst he had been at work. Glen still kept admiring this new look. 'I like the British makeover.'

We took turns showering and getting dressed and as Glen was getting ready, I did one final check of my small bag which contained the small plastic wallet storing my passport, J-1 visa, my I-94, some American dollar bills and travellers' cheques, and of course, a book which I aimed to finish reading on my flight home. I also kept my wallet, new frames, (that I had bought in Washington DC), various receipts and small bits of paper inside the plastic wallet, that were of no use but just sentimental, including the passport from the Holocaust Museum.

It was a good job the suitcases had wheels, as they were impossible to lift. These were the three suitcases that had I bought from Walmart. They were packed full; not just of clothes but books, paperwork and some gifts that students had given me when I left the school; memories of my year in North Carolina.

When I arrived at the airport in Washington, DC, each suitcase was weighed and all three were over the limit. The baggage handler put a sticker on the heaviest one to warn the baggage handlers.

'You are allowed to take this red one, at this weight, but the other two are over the limit. You will need to make them lighter', she said in a friendly manner.

The red case was indeed heavy and contained many things I had accumulated during my time here. I opened the two heavy cases in the departure lounge and started to empty them, as much as I could. Some of the gifts that the students gave me had to go and books which I left in a pile next to a steel bin. It was sad and difficult to leave these things behind. They were not just items, but memories, including a rubber alligator, that one student had given to me, which I had to keep, as a reminder – ridiculous to say that, after all the children I have taught over the years, but it just seemed more poignant, this time.

It was kind of Glen to drive me to the airport and after saying our emotional 'goodbyes', he left as I looked back. I had grown attached to him, his way of life, Washington, DC and my 'American life' – I was saying goodbye to everything.

42

07 August 2004

As the plane flew south, an announcement stated that we were flying over North Carolina. I could barely see the highways and the many towns that were normally thirty or forty miles apart quickly moved closer together as the plane ascended further into the sky. The forests that separated all of these towns slowly merged into one. It was a place in the world where I was once lost.

An elderly woman sat next to me, reading a magazine. Dressed in a dark-blue jacket and skirt and sitting upright, she smiled as I looked at her.

'Hello.' She spoke in an American accent, raising her shoulders from her small frame, as if pleased to meet me.

I remembered an expression my dad often used: 'It costs nothing to smile at someone.' I smiled at her as I thought of him.

The flight attendant arrived serving free refreshments.

'Would you like anything, sir?' she asked, in a southern drawl.

I looked up, distracted by her sudden arrival. 'Could I have a glass of sweet white wine, please?'

'Anything else with that, sir?'

'Do you have peanuts, please?'

'Would you like anything, madam?'

'I wi-y-ll have the same, please.'

I smiled as the flight attendant placed the glasses of wine and small foiled packets of peanuts on our tray tables. We thanked her before she moved on to serve other passengers.

'Are yew going anywhere naace?' my neighbour quietly asked.

'I am flying back ... home.'

'Is tha-y-t to England?'

'Yes.'

'I assumed you were Brid-ish.'

I grinned. 'Where do you live?'

239

'In Boone, North Carolina.'

'I remember seeing a sign for that town once?'

'It's near the Blue Ridge Mountains.'

'Oh yes.' Fond memories flooded my mind. 'There are so many towns in North Carolina I never visited.'

'Did yew visit the Blue Ridge Mountains?'

'We drove there with friends last October and I loved it. I remember it felt ... peaceful and looked stunning.'

'You can see the mountains from my house. I find them inspiring and love looking at the-y-m every day.' She continued, 'Tha-y-t was the fall!'

'It was. I cannot imagine living there!' She tittered in response. 'Are you going anywhere nice?' I asked.

She hesitated. 'I am visiting my son and his wife, who live in Cheshire. My daughter-in-law is Brid-ish.'

'That's nice. Is this your first trip to England?'

'My second.' She blushed yet looked unhappy.

'Oh yes?' I looked at her with intrigue.

'I am visiting my first grandchild.'

'Congratulations.'

'That's nice of yew to say but it's strange when your own children have their own children. It makes me feel...old!' She laughed, as she looked at her lap.

'I hope you don't mind me asking, what is the baby's name?' 'Charlotte.'

'That sounds rather British.' I spoke in an affected, posh accent.

'Do yew think so?' She looked proud.

'I am Paul.'

Her frail hand shook mine. 'I'm ... Charlotte. I'm pleased to meet yew.' Her small face glowed.

'Your name is Charlotte. Oh!'

She giggled. 'Yes. They named my granddaughter after me, it was sweet of them.'

'That's really nice.'

I detected sadness in her face.

'They called her Charlotte-Rose. What about yew, Paul? Are yew

240

going home to family?'

'Yes … and to a new start.'

'That sounds interesting'

I appreciated her zest for life and her deepening curiosity. 'Are you travelling alone, Charlotte?'

She looked down and then back at me, blinking, several times, before answering.

'My husband died a few weeks ago, and it's strange to be travelling alone.' She hesitated. 'My son and daughter-in-law took us to London and to Scotland the last time. Have you ever been to those places?'

'I am so sorry to hear that.' I looked down at my lap.

'It's fine. I am eighty-one years old and see life as an adventure!

'So, have yew been there?'

'Sorry?'

'Have you been to London or Scotland?'

'Oh, yes. I lived in London for several years.'

'London must be exciting?'

'There is always lots going on, but it's nice to get away. I love Scotland too and went there many times when I was a child.' I looked at her again as she nodded.

'That is amazing.' I added as I shook my head in disbelief.

'I don't follow?'

'I hope I look as good as you when I'm eighty-one.'

'Oh, that's very kind.'

'What's the secret?'

'I walk most days. Strange for an American, I know. I drink plenty of water and eat healthy food. I have never smoked, but I like the odd glass of wine', she added.

'There is nothing wrong in that!'

Joy, wisdom and love seemed to radiate from her soul.

She raised her plastic wine glass. 'Chin-chin', she said, as her plastic glass touched mine.

'Here's to your new granddaughter and your new adventure!'

'And here's to your new start.' She was sweeter than the wine. 'Did you live in North Carolina?'

'Yes.' I thought to myself, yesterday, North Carolina was my home; today, it is my past.

'What job did yew do here?'

'I was a teacher.'

'I used to be a teacher too, before I took retirement.'

'I can't believe that! I mean, I can! You sound intelligent.' I said, clumsily.

'I don't think I could be a teacher now.'

'That's incredible!'

'I bet the kids loved your accent.'

'I think they did. I had some nice students and some … interesting ones.'

'I bet. What do you think of Americans?' Her expression changed into a sudden look of seriousness and uncertainty as she waited for my response.

'You know, everyone I met was friendly and warm.' I looked at her again and sighed. 'I'm sad to leave it all behind.'

'Maybe you will come back, one day?'

'Maybe I will?'

'I bet you drove a lot?'

'Funny you should say that, when I gave that leased car back, the mileage read: seventy-two thousand miles! Can you believe?'

'North Carolina is a big state.'

'I know.'

Her eyes seemed to pierce my soul as if she knew more about me than I realised. I could clearly see her pupils.

'The highways can confuse you, don't you think?'

'Yes! The amount of times I got lost, was just … ridiculous.' Again, I laughed. 'It's typical, I left just as I got used to all the roads and those green exit signs.'

'I still sometimes take the wrong exit when I am driving, it's all very confusing, even for an old American like me!'

'You are still driving?'

'It gives me independence.' She paused before speaking again. 'I'm sure you got lost a few times, along your way, in North Carolina, Paul?'

As the plane flew higher, I looked back at her, and there seemed to be a peculiar moment between us and I thought about what she just said.

'So, what brought yew to North Carolina, Paul?'

'Do you really want to know?'

I laughed as she gestured with both of her hands in front of her, palms up as she shrugged her shoulders.

'How long have you got?'

'About nine hours!' We both laughed.

After some time talking and sipping my wine, we started to relax and I looked out of the window reflecting on my year in North Carolina. I looked back at Charlotte who was drifting in and out of sleep with her head bowing up and down. She had placed her cup of wine in the cup-holder and I think she only drank one sip when we had celebrated.

I stared through the window again and reflected on the journey I had taken and how I changed with the help of North Carolina, Glen and everyone else I had met.

I had not actually driven 72,000 miles but I had travelled thousands of miles; journeys, mainly made on my own, and for the most part, I had been lost in myself. It was as if those confusing green signs perched high above me and rocking in the wind, had directed me to the point where I had eventually found my direction in life.

Life, as well as driving, in North Carolina, had not always been easy; there were twists and turns, ups and downs, different directions, red lights and green lights, right routes and wrong routes but mostly big, open, flat, straight roads – which I had driven down, alone. I was once that child, who placed the blue peg moving that green plastic car past American styled, white plastic buildings, stopping on the lucky and the not-so-lucky squares on that board of *The Game of Life,* surrounded by my family. Many years later, I had driven that green car following a long and winding road past American white houses, monuments and buildings, stopping on lucky and the not-so-lucky squares on the road of life.

I looked out of the aeroplane window one last time as we flew

243

higher and all I could see was the sheer expanse of the huge green forests which seemed to have all merged into one green blanket, carpeting the floors of the Carolinas.

Somewhere down there, on that road of life, I had finally found myself.

I relaxed and lay back in my seat and looked once more at Charlotte, who was now fast asleep. I remember the way she looked at me with those piercing blue eyes that seemed to look deep into my soul for those few minutes, as if she knew everything I had been through and the reason for my journey.

I grew tired and fell asleep.

I woke up feeling surprised as we had already landed and most of the passengers had left the plane. Sadly, there was no sign of Charlotte or her wine glass. I looked down at her seat and on it was a small piece of folded paper, which I picked up and put into my pocket before quickly collecting my small rucksack from the overhead locker and rushing clumsily half-awake down the aisle.

As I stepped off the plane, the words from the song 'Easy Ride', by Madonna I once listened to, entered my mind: 'I go round and round just like a circle'. As my feet touched the ground, I had indeed come full circle. I could see the picture clearly now, and I was finally home. I looked up at the blue sky, feeling the sun on my face and the cooler wind.

Thoughts flooded my mind and as I smiled, I walked slowly towards the airport building. I stopped to look back at the plane. The bright sunshine made me squint and I placed my hand over my eyes to see the haze from the hot engines of the plane that had carried me from North Carolina, a place that had guided me through a difficult time in my life.

Again, thoughts flooded back about the countless roads and thousands of miles I had travelled and how, sometimes, I had fallen down along the way. I remembered the isolation I had felt and that cold

North Carolinian wind blowing over the lonely cotton field as each plant danced and that kind woman who appeared and lifted me high into the sky away from my sadness and loneliness – did God help me to look at my life and to move forward at that precise moment? I remembered the sight of my empty apartment as I entered it for the first time and as I left it for the last, and in that short time between, the difficulties I had experienced, the exhilaration America had given me and how much I had grown. I thought about the expanse and the quietness of the Carolinas, the large and empty blue skies, the heat of the sun, all the driving, fast-food and home-cooked food, the misty mountains, that final view of Washington, D.C. and Glen's smile and his and my tears of acceptance at the airport as I walked away.

I thought about the friends I had made, Hayley's infectious laugh and Tee's continual support, Ade's endearing giggles, the laughter of the students growing up all too soon and the hurdles – there were so many of them. I thought of Halise, as without her I may never have taken that journey. And about Nick, and I was finally thankful that he had entered my life. Without him, I would never had taken this journey in search of treasure; it was only later that I realised my treasure and happiness could not be searched for, in any country, or in any part of the world - it had always been in my heart.

I suddenly remembered that piece of paper tucked inside my jeans pocket. I took it out and slowly unfolded it and smiled as I read Charlotte's kind words. I looked up and confidently walked ahead, and as the glass doors opened, so did my future.

The End

All of us have a story to tell.

We are all authors.

If we tell our stories in such a way, describing our journey, where each stop along the way was a lesson, then we can help others tell their stories too.

In these stories are endless lessons towards wisdom, wellbeing and resonance.

In an interconnected way of telling stories, we can help, uplift and raise people towards their true purpose and light.

Ameet Bilal Shah, July 2016

Present time

Halise lives in Melbourne, Australia. She is happily married to a different man, and they have two children. We keep in contact through social media.

Glen met someone new and they moved to Malta. We kept in touch by email, became good friends and I met up with him when I visited my family in Malta, a year later.

I keep in touch with many of the teachers I met in North Carolina through social media but, sadly, I lost contact with Ade.

I have contentment.

LOST FOR 72,000 MILES

P.G. Wood was born and raised in Rochdale, England. He moved to London in the late 80's in order to study a science degree at the University of Greenwich. He taught at various schools in Northern England and Southern England and the USA. *Lost for 72,000 Miles* is his first book.

Acknowledgements

I would like to thank many people for helping bringing this book alive. In particular, Ann Christine Lelievre for your motivation, Carlos Figueirdo and other IT technicians who helped me with various technical issues, the late Sylvia Booth for kindly buying me a laptop, and friends and family for your encouragement. Thank you to Belle Mundy for the copy-editing and Lisa Chernin-Newton for your proof-reading – thanks to you both for your professionalism, advice and dedication, and, lastly, the American Teaching Programme, for giving me an amazing lifetime opportunity.

Living in Bookham, Surrey for a short period, gave me time, peace and solitude to write.

Printed in Great Britain
by Amazon